EDEXCEL

CERTIFICATE OF ACHIEVEMENT in Mathematics

Sue Bright • Dan Birkett • Keith Pledger

GW00771613

EDEXCEL
FOUNDATION

Heinemann Educational Publishers
Halley Court, Jordan Hill, Oxford, OX2 8EJ
a division of Reed Educational & Professional Publishing Ltd
Heinemann is a registered trademark of Reed Educational & Professional Publishing Ltd

OXFORD MELBOURNE AUCKLAND
JOHANNESBURG BLANTYRE GABORONE
IBADAN PORTSMOUTH NH (USA) CHICAGO

© Sue Bright, Dan Birkett and Keith Pledger, 1998

First published 1998

ISBN 0 435 53233 2

99 00 01 02 10 9 8 7 6 5 4 3 2

Designed and typeset by Tech-Set Ltd, Gateshead, Tyne and Wear

Printed and bound in Spain by Edelvives

Acknowledgements

Cover photo by Photonica/Pedro Lobo
Cover design by Miller, Craig and Cocking

Publishing team

Editorial
Philip Ellaway
Sarah Caton

Design
Phil Richards
Colette Jacquelin

Production
David Lawrence
Jo Morgan

About this book

This book is designed to provide students with the best possible preparation for their Edexcel Certificate of Achievement in Mathematics. The authors are examiners and task moderators themselves and have a good understanding of all the Examination Council's requirements.

About the Certificate of Achievement

The Edexcel Certificate of Achievement in Mathematics is an entry level award certifying achievement at Level 1 (Bronze), Level 2 (Silver) and Level 3 (Gold) of the National Curriculum. Successful performance at entry level gives students access to GCSE Mathematics and GNVQ and NVQ awards at Level 1.

Finding your way around

To help you find your way around when you are studying use the

- **edge marks** (shown on the front page) – these help you find the right section quickly

- **contents lists** – these list the headings that identify key syllabus ideas covered in the book so that you can turn straight to them. Codes are included to show which part of the syllabus you are covering. For example, **BNc** means the content relates to the **B**ronze section, covering the **N**umber part of the syllabus subsection **c** (the third paragraph).

Remembering key ideas

We have provided clear explanations of the key ideas and techniques throughout the book. The Remember boxes summarize the important information students need to know and remember.

Bronze Contents

1 Numbers up to 10

To count objects you need to know the numbers up to 10 in order.

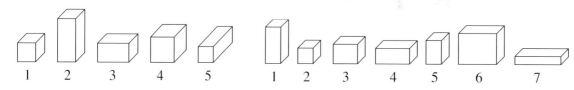

1   2   3   4   5   6   7   8   9   10

You use the numbers like this:

Count these boxes.   Count these boxes.

There are 5 boxes.   There are 7 boxes.

Exercise 1A

1   Count these eggs.

2   Count these boxes.

3   Count these cups.

4   Count these melons.

5   Count these spoons.

6   Count these cars.

How many?

To answer the question, 'How many?', you need to count.

Example

How many tyres?

Count the tyres.

Answer: 4 tyres

Exercise 1B

1   How many t-shirts?

2   How many CD's?

3   How many videos?

4   How many bananas?

5   How many pencils?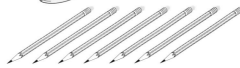

6   How many nails?

Remember To count objects, write the numbers next to the objects as you count them.

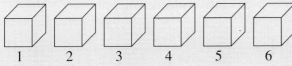   There are 6 cubes.

Check your answers. Count again.

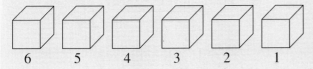   There are 6 cubes.

2 Words up to 10

You can write numbers in words or figures:

figures	1	2	3	4	5	6	7	8	9	10
words	one	two	three	four	five	six	seven	eight	nine	ten

Example

Write in words: **a** 5   **b** 9

Answer:

a   5 is five   **b**   9 is nine

Example

Write in figures: **a**   four   **b**   three

Answer:

a   four is 4   **b**   three is 3

Exercise 2A

1   Write in words: **a** 2   **b** 4   **c** 7
                       d 10   **e** 6   **f** 3

2   Write in figures:
    a   one   **b**   five   **c**   nine   **d**   eight   **e**   seven
    f   two   **g**   three **h**   six   **i**   four   **j**   ten

Example

How many cans?

Write the number as a word.

Answer: seven

Example

Count these.

Write the number as a word.

Answer: four

Exercise 2B

In this exercise give your answers in **words**.

1   How many counters?

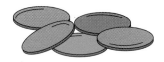

2   How many burgers?

3   Count these.

4   How many cubes?

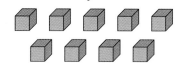

5   Count these.

6   Count these.

7   How many pens?

8   How many oranges?

9   Count these.

10   Count these.

Dot patterns

You can use dot patterns to stand for numbers. Count the dots to find how many there are.

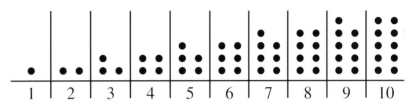

Example

Write in words.

Count the dots.

Answer: three

Example

Draw 4 dots.

Count as you draw.

Count again to check. Answer:

Exercise 2C

1   Count the dots and write your answers in words

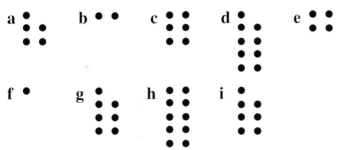

a **b** **c** **d** **e**

f **g** **h** **i**

2   Draw these dots.   **a** seven   **b** one   **c** ten   **d** five

Remember Make sure you can write numbers in figures and words.
It might help to say the numbers out loud.

| 1 one | 2 two | 3 three | 4 four | 5 five |
| 6 six | 7 seven | 8 eight | 9 nine | 10 ten |

3 Comparing sizes

You need to be able to compare sizes, lengths and heights.

You use these words to compare two objects:
bigger, smaller, longer, shorter, taller.

Size	**Height**	**Length**
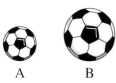		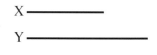

A is **smaller** than B. | P is **taller** than Q. | X is **shorter** than Y.
B is **bigger** than A. | Q is **shorter** than P. | Y is **longer** than X.

Example

The bottle is taller than the glass. True or false?

Look at the picture and compare the heights.

  Answer: True

Example

A is shorter than B. True or false?

A | 1 2 3 4 5 6 7 8 9 10 11 12 13 14 15 16 17 18 19 20 21 22 23 24 25 26 27 28 29 30

B | 1 2 3 4 5 6 7 8 9 10 11 12 13 14 15

Compare the lengths.   Answer: False

Exercise 3A

1 The pylon is taller than the tower.

True or false?

2 The car is longer than the lorry.

True or false?

3 The plate is smaller than the bowl. True or false?

4 The flagpole is shorter than the tree. True or false?

5 The parcel is bigger than the letter. True or false?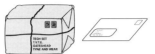

Example

Draw a ball bigger than this one.

Answer: *or*   *or*   *or*

All these balls are bigger than the one above.

Exercise 3B

1 Draw a line longer than this one.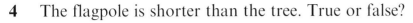

2 Draw a box smaller than this one.

3 Draw a pin-man taller than this one.

4 Draw a brick shorter than this one.

For more than two objects use these words to compare sizes: biggest, smallest, longest, shortest, tallest.

Size	**Height**	**Length**
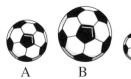		X ——————— Y ————————— Z ———————
A B C	P Q R	
B is bigger than A. B is bigger than C. B is the **biggest**.	P is taller than Q. P is taller than R. P is the **tallest**.	Y is longer than X. Y is longer than Z. Y is the **longest**.
C is smaller than B, C is smaller than A. C is the **smallest**.	Q is shorter than R. Q is shorter than P. Q is the **shortest**.	Z is shorter than Y, Z is shorter than X. Z is the **shortest**.

Example

Which tree is the shortest?
A is shorter than B, and
A is shorter than C.

A   B   C

Compare the heights.

Answer: A

1   Which sunflower is the biggest?

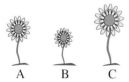

A   B   C

2   Which is the tallest?

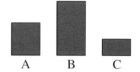

A   B   C

3   Which is the longest?

4   Which is the smallest?

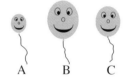

A   B   C

5   Which is the tallest?

A   B   C

6   Which is the shortest?

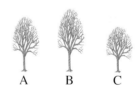

A   B   C

7   Which is the tallest?

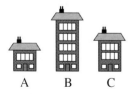

A   B   C

8   Which is the biggest?

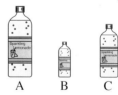

A   B   C

Remember these words to describe sizes.

tallest   shortest   longest

biggest   smallest

4 Patterns of two

Patterns are all around us. To continue a pattern you need to spot the part
that repeats.

Here is a pattern.   ● ■ ● ■ ? ? ? ?   This part repeats.

Draw the next 4 shapes.   ● ■ ● ■ ● ■ ● ■

Here is a pattern.   ◪◪◪◪   This part repeats.

Finish the pattern.   ◪◪◪◪

Example

Copy the pattern.   ☐☐☐☐ ? ? ? ?

Draw the next 4 shapes.   This part repeats.

Answer: ☐☐☐☐☐☐☐☐

Exercise 4A

1 Copy the pattern.

●○●○ ? ? ? ?

Draw the next 4 shapes.

2 Copy the pattern.

☐●☐● ? ? ?

Draw the next 3 shapes.

3 Copy and finish the pattern.

4 Copy and finish the pattern.

Example

What comes next?   ☐△☐△☐△☐
Draw it.

Answer: △

Exercise 4B

1 What comes next? Draw it.

2 What comes next? Draw it.

3 What comes next? Draw it.

4 What comes next? Draw it.

X • X • X

Number patterns

These 2 repeat. → 1   2,   1   2   1   2

These 2 repeat. → 5   0,   5   0   5   0

Example

What comes next?   4   6   4   6   4   Write it down.

Answer: 6

Exercise 4C

1 What comes next?
3 5 3 5 3 5 3 5
Write it down.

2 What comes next?
1 7 1 7 1 7 1
Write it down.

3 What comes next?
8 5 8 5 8 5 8
Write it down.

4 What comes next?
6 9 6 9 6 9 6
Write it down.

5 What comes next?
7 4 7 4 7 4
Write it down.

Remember In a pattern look for the shapes that repeat.

These two repeat. → ☐ △, ☐ △ ☐ △ ☐

In a number pattern look for the numbers that repeat.

Say the numbers to **hear** the pattern.

These two repeat. → 5   8,   5   8   5

5 Describing shapes

There are many different kinds of shapes. You can describe most shapes using one of these words:

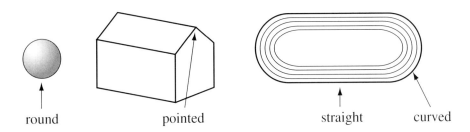

round   pointed   straight   curved

Example

Describe this ruler.
Choose the best word.
Answer: straight

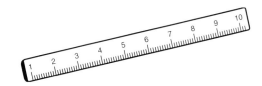

Exercise 5A

Choose your answers from this list: round   straight   curved   pointed

1   Describe this banana.

2   Describe this orange.

3   Describe this hat.

4   Describe this ladder.

5   Describe this shape.

6   Describe this line.

7   Describe this line. ———

8   Describe this shape.

Example

How many | ?

Count the | Answer: 5

How many \ ?

Count the \   Answer: 3

Exercise 5B

1

   a How many ☐ ?

   b How many ▨ ?

   c How many ■ ?

2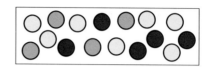

   a How many ● ?

   b How many ● ?

   c How many ○ ?

3

   a How many ▲ ?

   b How many ▲ ?

   c How many △ ?

4

   a How many ▭ ?

   b How many ▬ ?

   c How many ▬ ?

Example

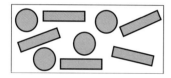

How many straight shapes?   Answer: 5

How many round shapes?   Answer: 4

Exercise 5C

1

   a How many round shapes?

   b How many pointed shapes?

2

   a How many straight lines?

   b How many curved lines?

3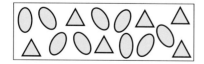

   a How many curved shapes?

   b How many pointed shapes?

4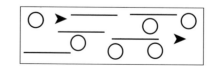

   a How many round shapes?

   b How many pointed shapes?

   c How many straight lines?

6 Adding

You need to be able to add two sets of objects together
and find the total number.

Count out 3 counters.

Add 2 counters.

 and  makes

   3   and   2   makes   5

Example

How many apples? and makes .....

Count out counters. and

Count all the counters.  and makes

   5   and   4   makes   9

Answer: 9 apples

Exercise 6A

Use counters to help you.

1 How many counters?

 makes .....

2 How many pens?

 makes .....

3 How many drinks?

 makes .....

4 How many keys?

 makes .....

5 How many cubes?

6 How many CDs?

7 How many dots?

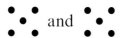 and

8 How many cups?

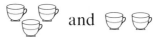 and

9 How many eggs?

 and

10 How many t-shirts?

and

Example

How many scissors?  and

Count the scissors.   2   and   6   makes   8

Answer: 8 scissors

Exercise 6B

1 How many counters?

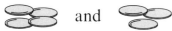 and

2 How many drinks?

 and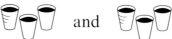

3 How many ice creams?

 and

4 How many burgers?

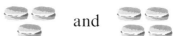 and

5 How many buns?

 and

6 How many balls?

 and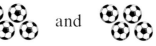

7 How many cubes?

 and

8 How many dots?

 and

9 How many candles?

 and

10 How many coins?

 and

Example

There are 2 birds. 2 more come.
How many birds now?

2   and   2   makes   4

Answer: 4 birds

Exercise 6C

1   There are 5 people.
2 more join them.
How many people now?

2   There are 7 cars in the park.
3 more come.
How many cars now?

3   There are 4 cubes in a box.
2 more are put in.
How many cubes in the box?

4   There are 6 coins in a purse.
3 more are put in.
How many coins in the purse?

5   There are 3 oranges in a bag.
5 more are put in.
How many oranges in the bag?

Remember You can use your fingers to help you add.

How many balls?

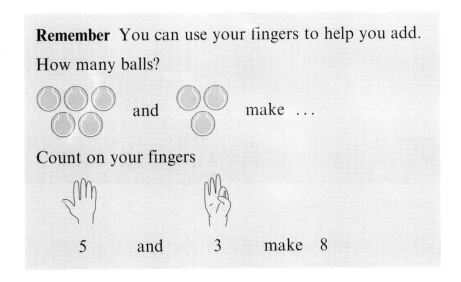

5   and   3   make   8

7 Subtracting

Count out 6 cubes. Take away 2 cubes (cover 2). 4 left

6 take away 2 leaves 4.

This is called subtracting.

Exercise 7A

Use cubes to help you find how many are left.

1 take away

2 take away

3 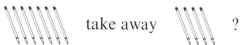 take away

4  take away

5 take away

6 take away

7 take away

8 take away

9 take away

10 take away

Example

take away ?

Count the pencils.

  7   take away   4   Cover 4   3 left

Answer: 3 pencils

Exercise 7B

How many are left?

1  take away

2 take away

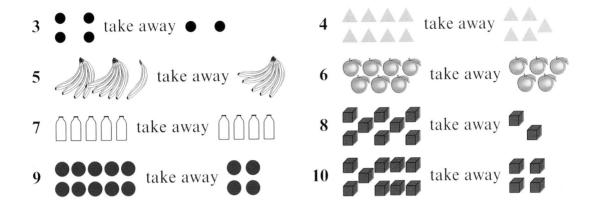

3 ● ● take away ● ●

4 take away

5 take away

6 take away

7 take away

8 take away

9 ● ● ● ● ● take away ● ●

10 take away

Example

There are 7 cherries. You eat 2 cherries. How many are left?

take away

7   take away   2   leaves 5

Answer: 5 cherries

Exercise 7C

1 There are 8 cars in the street. 5 cars leave.
How many are left?

2 There are 6 cubes in a box. 3 cubes are taken out.
How many are left?

3 There are 9 people in a room. 2 people leave.
How many are left?

4 There are 10 coins in a purse. 6 coins are taken out.
How many are left?

5 There are 6 eggs in a box. 4 eggs are used.
How many are left?

Remember You can use your fingers to help you take away.

take away   leaves

Hold up 6 fingers   Put 3 down   3 left.

6 take away 3 leaves 3

8 More, less or the same?

To compare amounts and numbers you use the words
more or fewer.

John's pens   Kyle's pens

John has 4 pens.   Kyle has 2 pens.

John has **more** pens than Kyle.
Kyle has **fewer** pens than John.

Example

Jody's chocolates   Nikki's chocolates

Who has fewer chocolates?

Count the chocolates.

    Jody: 5   Nikki: 8

So Jody has fewer chocolates.

Answer: Jody

Exercise 8A

1   Mike's pencils   Ali's pencils

Who has more pencils?

2   Abbi's cards   Sue's cards

Who has fewer cards?

3   Balvir's   Kirsty's
     sandwiches   sandwiches

Who has more sandwiches?

4   Carmen's apples   Jake's apples

Who has fewer apples?

Jason's oranges   Carly's oranges

Jason and Carly have the **same** number of oranges.

Example

Patrick's cherries

Lucy has the same number of cherries as Patrick.
How many cherries has Lucy?

Count the cherries.
Patrick has 5 cherries. Lucy has the same.

Answer: 5 cherries

Exercise 8B

1   Saleem's CDs

    Marissa has the same number of CDs as Saleem.
    How many CDs has Marissa?

2   Leanne's videos

    Rory has the same number of videos as Leanne.
    How many videos has Rory?

3   Laura's fish

    Simon has the same number of fish as Laura.
    How many fish has Simon?

How many more?

Here are two piles of cubes.
Pile X has 5 cubes.
Pile Y has 2 cubes.
Pile X has **more** than pile Y.

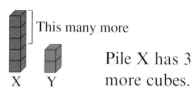

This many more

Pile X has 3 more cubes.

Example

a Which pile has more cubes?

b How many more?

a Count the cubes.
X has 5 cubes. Y has 6 cubes.
So Y has more cubes.

Answer: Y

b Count how many more.

Answer: 1 cube

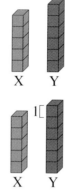

Exercise 8C

a Which pile has more cubes?   **b** How many more?

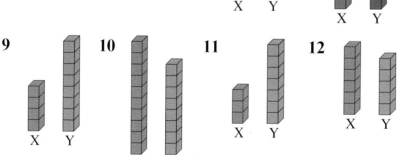

Here are two piles of cubes.
Pile X has 7 cubes.
Pile Y has 3 cubes.

Y has 4 less than X.
Y has 4 fewer than X.

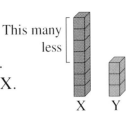

This many less

Pile Y has **less** cubes than X.
Pile Y has **fewer** cubes than X.] These mean the same.

Example

a Which pile has less cubes?   **b** How many less?

a Count them.
X has 3 cubes. Y has 6 cubes. X has less cubes.

Answer: X

b Count how many less.

Answer: 3 cubes

Exercise 8D

a Which pile has less cubes?   **b** How many less?

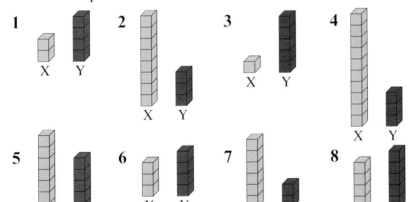

Which pile has fewer cubes?   How many fewer?

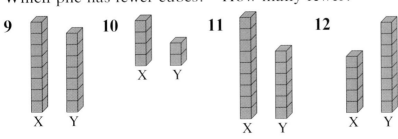

9 Ordering

It is useful to know which number is biggest or smallest.
You can then write numbers in order of size.

When you count you say the numbers **in order**.
The numbers get bigger as you count.

On a number line:

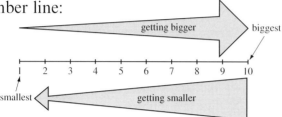

Example

Which is the biggest?

3   5

Look at the cubes in the picture.
5 is biggest.

Answer: 5

Example

Which is the smallest?

7   4

Answer: 4

Exercise 9A

1   Which is bigger?

  a 8 4   **b** 6 7   **c** 10 8

  d 9 2   **e** 8 9   **f** 5 7

2   Which is smaller?

  a 3 6   **b** 9 7   **c** 4 6

  d 8 5   **e** 7 3   **f** 1 9

Example

Which is biggest?

  2 9 7

Look at the cubes.
Answer: 9

Example

Which is smallest?

  6 5 3

Answer: 3

Exercise 9B

1 Which is biggest?
  a 9 4 7   **b** 3 6 1   **c** 2 8 5
  d 6 1 4 2   **e** 8 6 3 4   **f** 9 7 5 6

2 Which is smallest?
  a 8 3 5   **b** 2 1 6   **c** 8 6 4
  d 6 2 5 1   **e** 4 9 7 6   **f** 5 10 7 4

Putting numbers in order

Example

Write these in order
  4   3   8   1
Start with the smallest.

Which is smallest?   1 ⎤
Which is next smallest?   3 ⎥ ─ Write
Which is next smallest?   4 ⎥   them
Which is next smallest?   8 ⎦   in this
                                  order.
Answer: 1 3 4 8 ───────┘

Example

Write these in order
  5   9   7   2
Start with the biggest.

Which is biggest?   9 ⎤
Which is next biggest?   7 ⎥ ─ Write
Which is next biggest?   5 ⎥   them
Which is next biggest?   2 ⎦   in this
                                 order.
Answer: 9 7 5 2 ───────┘

Exercise 9C

1 Write these in order. Start with the smallest.

  a 8 6 3 4   **b** 9 6 5 7   **c** 6 4 5 2
  d 7 4 6 5   **e** 8 9 10 4   **f** 5 6 4 7

2 Write these in order. Start with the biggest.
  a 2 4 9 1   **b** 7 3 4 8   **c** 8 9 6 3
  d 5 6 3 4   **e** 2 8 3 4   **f** 7 5 1 2

Hint: To see which number is biggest, use your fingers.

Which is biggest?   5   2

5 is biggest. 2 is smallest.   5   2

10 Where does it belong?

You can sort shapes into sets by their important features.
For example:

by **colour**:
this shape is red

by **number of sides**:
this shape has 4 sides

To find where a shape belongs, look for shapes with the
same features.

Example

Where does this shape belong? •

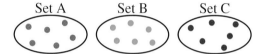

The shape belongs in set C
because all the shapes in set C
are red.

Example

Where does this shape belong? ◢

The shape belongs in set B
because all the shapes in
set B have 3 sides.

Exercise 10A

1 Where does ■ belong?

3 Where does ▰ belong?

Hint: are they sorted by
shape or colour?

2 Where does ☆ belong?

4 Where does ■ belong?

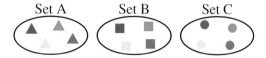

Hint: shape or colour?

Sorting other objects

You can sort other objects into sets by their features.

Example

Where does this object belong?

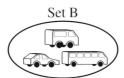

It belongs to set A because it has 2 wheels.

Exercise 10B

1 Where does  belong?

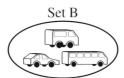

2 Where does 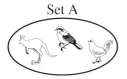 belong?

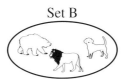

3 Where does 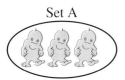 belong?

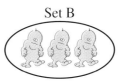

Remember To sort objects into sets, look for objects with the same features.

These bottles are all green.   These shapes are all round.

11 Sides and corners

You can describe a shape by how many sides and corners
it has.

To count the number of sides, use your fingers.

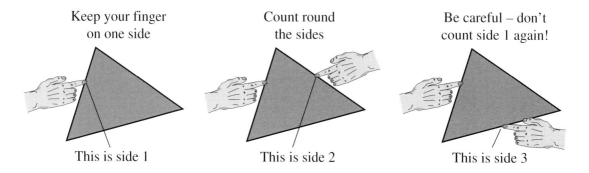

This shape has 3 sides.

Now count the corners.

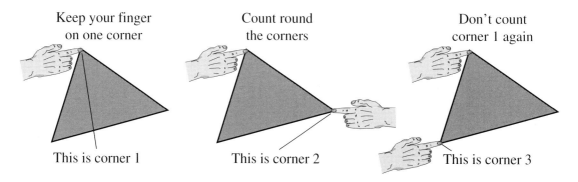

This shape has 3 corners.

Exercise 11A

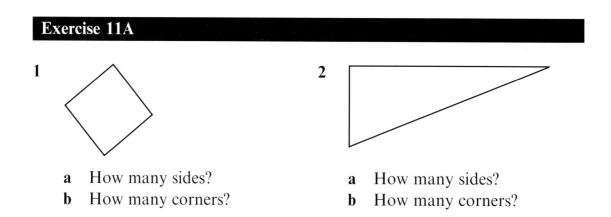

1
  a How many sides?
  b How many corners?

2
  a How many sides?
  b How many corners?

3

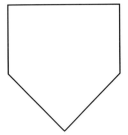

a   How many sides?
b   How many corners?

4

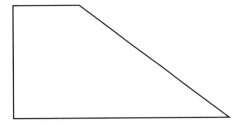

a   How many sides?
b   How many corners?

5

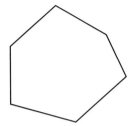

a   How many sides?
b   How many corners?

6

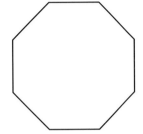

a   How many sides?
b   How many corners?

7

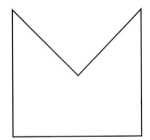

a   How many sides?
b   How many corners?

8

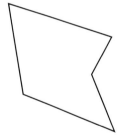

a   How many sides?
b   How many corners?

9

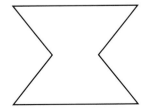

a   How many sides?
b   How many corners?

10

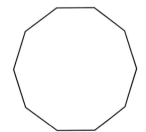

a   How many sides?
b   How many corners?

12 Cubes

You can use cubes to make many different shapes.
Count the cubes to find out how many there are.

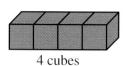

4 cubes

3 cubes

Example

How many cubes are here?
Count them.

Answer: 4 cubes

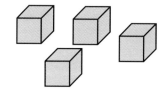

Exercise 12A

1   How many cubes?

2   How many cubes?

3   How many cubes?

4   How many cubes?

5   How many cubes?

Example

How many cubes are in this shape?

Collect some cubes.
Make the shape.
Count the cubes in your shape.
Answer: 3 cubes

Exercise 12B

You will need some cubes.
Count the cubes in these shapes.

1

How many cubes?

2

How many cubes?

3

How many cubes?

4

How many cubes?

5

How many cubes?

6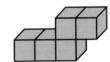

How many cubes?

7

How many cubes?

8

How many cubes?

9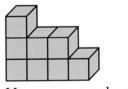

How many cubes?

10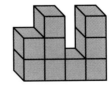

How many cubes?

Remember Take your shape apart to count the cubes.

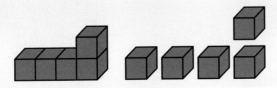

13 Counting shapes

You need to be able to sort and count shapes.

One type of shape:

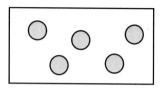
How many ⬤ in the box?

There are 5.

Two types of shape: ▲ and ▨

How many ▲ in the box?
There are 6.
How many ▨ in the box?
There are 3.

Example

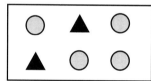
a How many ⬤ in the box?
b How many ▲ in the box?

a Count

Answer: 4

b Count ▲

Answer: 2

Exercise 13A

1

How many ▭ in the box?

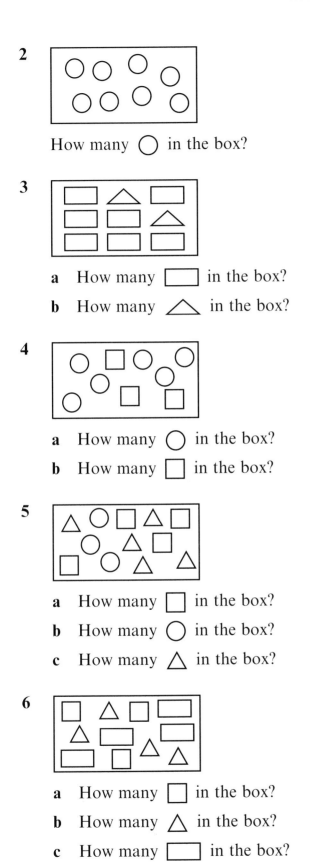

2

How many ◯ in the box?

3

a How many ▭ in the box?

b How many △ in the box?

4

a How many ◯ in the box?

b How many ☐ in the box?

5

a How many ☐ in the box?

b How many ◯ in the box?

c How many △ in the box?

6

a How many ☐ in the box?

b How many △ in the box?

c How many ▭ in the box?

14 Where and when?

You need to be able to describe where things are and when things happened.

Here are some words to describe **where** things are.

The crisps are **beside** the snack selection.
The chews are **above** the raisins.
The apple and pear mix is **under** the raisins.
The lemonade is **behind** the cola.
The snack selection is **on** the top shelf.
The apple and blackcurrant drink is **below** the crisps.

Exercise 14A

What is the missing word?

1 The pick and mix is _____ the crisps.

2 The orangeade is _____ the cola.

3 The cherryade is _____ the pick and mix.

4 The apple juice is _____ the bottom shelf.

5 The dried banana pieces are _____ the raisins.

6 The snack selection is _____ the raisins.

Here are some words to describe **when** things happen.

Example

A
Boil the kettle

before

B
You make the tea

A **before** B

Example

C
Throw away the can

after

D
You drink the cola

C **after** D

Exercise 14B

Write **before** or **after**.

1   A    B

Knock on the door   Go in

A . . . . B

2   C    D

Post the letter   Put the stamp on

C . . . . D

3   E   F

Put your helmet on   Ride a motorbike

E . . . . F

4   G   H

Answer the phone   The phone rings

G . . . . H

You can use **before** and **after** like this:

Example

John is **before** Kate.
Kate is **after** John.

Exercise 14C

Write **before** or **after**.

1

Matt is . . . . Jay

2

Sunil is . . . . Jane

3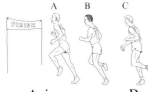

a   A is . . . . B
b   C is . . . . B

4

a   B is . . . . A
b   C is . . . . D

15 Calculator numbers

You can use a calculator to help you add numbers together. First you need to be able to read numbers from calculators.

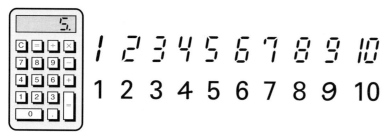

1 2 3 4 5 6 7 8 9 10

Example

Write the number shown on the calculator.

Answer: 6

Exercise 15A

Write the number shown on the calculator.

1

2

3

4

5

Example

Write the calculator number 🆎 as a figure.

Answer: 8

Example

Write the calculator number 5 in words.

Answer: five

Exercise 15B

1   Write the calculator numbers in words:

   a 3   **b** 9   **c** 5   **d** 4   **e** 7   **f** 10   **g** 8

2   Write the calculator numbers in figures:

   a 1   **b** 2   **c** 7   **d** 10   **e** 6   **f** 9   **g** 3

Example

Put the number seven on your calculator.
Write down the number.

Press   7

Answer: 7.   7

Exercise 15C

1   Put these numbers on your calculator.
   Write down the number.
   a five   **b** eight   **c** four   **d** two   **e** three   **f** ten

Remember Writing calculator numbers.
Don't write the dot!

Answer: 4

Silver Contents

1 Counting to 20

To count objects you need to know the numbers in order.

You know the numbers up to 10. This is how they continue to 20.

| 1 | 2 | 3 | 4 | 5 | 6 | 7 | 8 | 9 | 10 |
| 11 | 12 | 13 | 14 | 15 | 16 | 17 | 18 | 19 | 20 |

You can write numbers in words or figures.

figures 11   12   13   14   15   16   17   18   19   20
words eleven twelve thirteen fourteen fifteen sixteen seventeen eighteen nineteen twenty

This page will help you practise writing numbers up to 20.

Example

Write in words: **a** 15   **b** 19

Answer: **a** 15 is fifteen   **b** 19 is nineteen

Example

Write in figures: **a** sixteen   **b** eleven

Answer: **a** sixteen is 16   **b** eleven is 11

Exercise 1A

1 Write in words: **a** 14   **b** 17   **c** 12   **d** 11   **e** 19   **f** 20
2 Write in figures: **a** thirteen   **b** twenty   **c** eighteen
                       d fifteen   **e** twelve   **f** sixteen

Tens and units

You can use cubes to stand for numbers over ten.
Here are 13 cubes.
Start with a tower of 10.
Add the units you need.

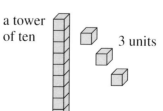

a tower of ten

3 units

1 ten 3 units is 13

Example

Draw 14 cubes.   Answer:

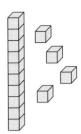

Exercise 1B

Draw:

a 15 cubes	**b** 12 cubes	**c** 18 cubes	**d** 11 cubes
e 13 cubes	**f** 17 cubes	**g** 19 cubes	**h** 16 cubes

Splitting numbers into tens and units

Example

Copy and complete: Count the cubes:

— ten and — units

Answer:
1 ten and 4 units

Exercise 1C

Copy and complete:

a

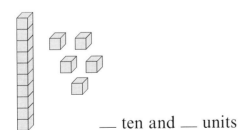

— ten and — units

b

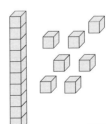

— ten and — units

c

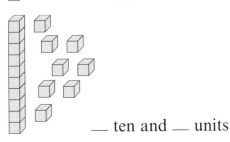

— ten and — units

d

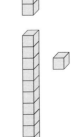

— ten and — unit

Example

Here are 17 cubes.

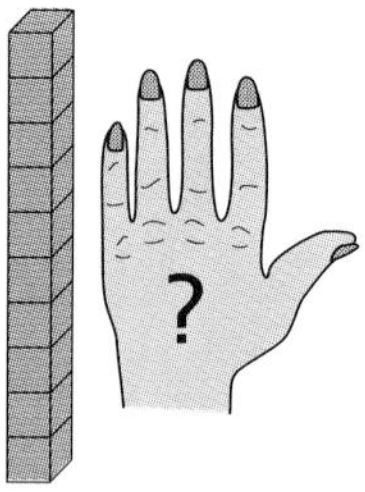

17 is

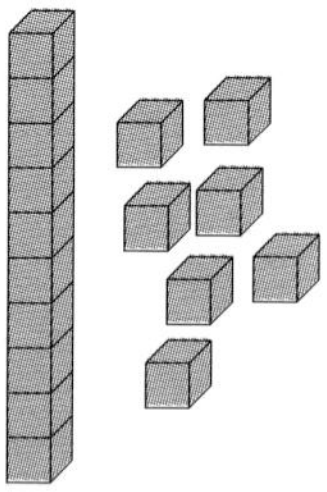

How many are hidden?

Answer: 7 cubes are hidden.

Exercise 1D

How many cubes are hidden?

1 13 cubes

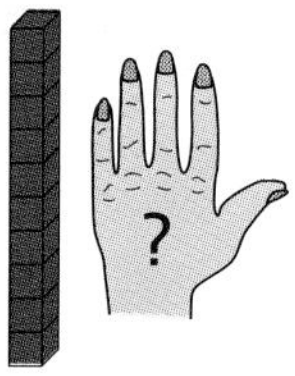

2 18 cubes

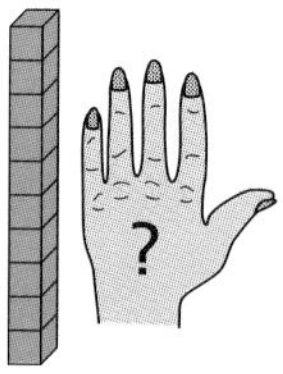

3 10 cubes

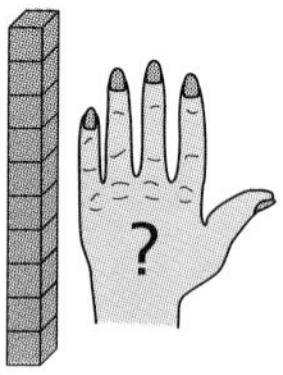

4 16 cubes

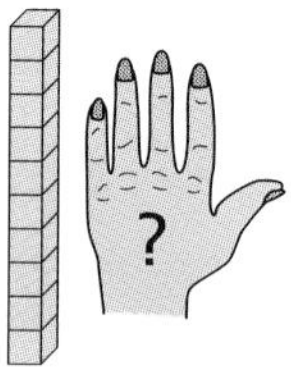

5 15 cubes

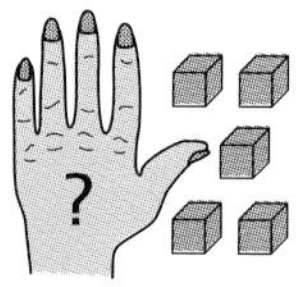

6 12 cubes

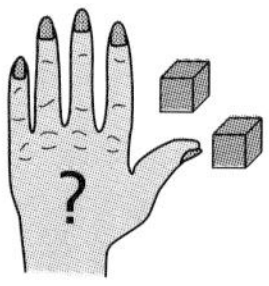

7 14 cubes

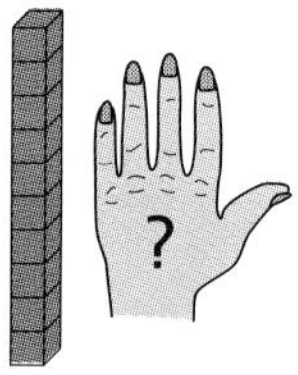

8 19 cubes

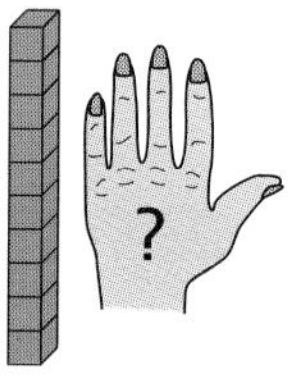

9 20 cubes

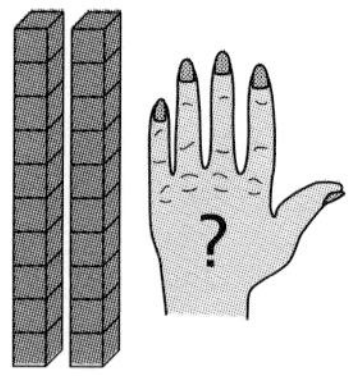

10 11 cubes

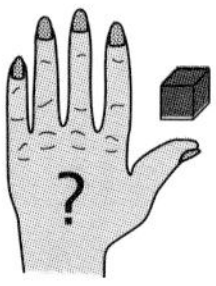

Remember You can write numbers in figures and words.
You already know the numbers up to 10.

11	eleven	15	fifteen	19	nineteen
12	twelve	16	sixteen	20	twenty
13	thirteen	17	seventeen		
14	fourteen	18	eighteen		

2 Repeating patterns

Here is a repeating pattern:

●●□●●□●●□

The pattern is: two of these ● then one of these □.

Remember: to continue a pattern, look for the part that repeats.

Example

Copy and complete this pattern.

□□●□□●□□ ?

Answer: □□●□□●□□●

Exercise 2A

Here are some repeating patterns. Copy and complete each one.

1 ●●△●●△●● ?   2 ♥◆◆♥◆◆♥◆ ?

3 □□□××□□×× ?   4 ●△△△●△△△ ?

Example

What comes next? Draw it.

 ?

Answer: ◎

Exercise 2B

What comes next? Draw it.

1 [bottle][bottle][Crisps][Crisps][bottle][bottle][Crisps] ?

2 [shirt][shirt][shirt][trousers][trousers][shirt][shirt][shirt][trousers] ?

3 ■■◇■■◇■■ ?

Making patterns

To make a pattern, start with a simple pattern. Then repeat it.

Example

Use ☐ and ◯ to make a pattern. Repeat it.

Answer:

   or

Exercise 2C

Make a repeating pattern with these shapes:

1 ☐△   **2** ◯△   **3** ▯☐

Number patterns

Patterns can be made from numbers too. Look for the part that repeats. Here is a repeating number pattern:

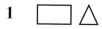 1   1   2   1   1   2   1   1   2
                  └── this part repeats

The pattern is: two 1s then one 2.

Example

What comes next? Write it down.

    3   2   2   3   2   2   3   ?

Answer: 2

The part that repeats is

   3   2   2   3   2   2   3   ?

The pattern is one 3, then two 2s. So after a 3 comes a 2.

Exercise 2D

What comes next? Write it down.

1 2   1   2   1   2   1   2   ?   **2** 1   3   3   1   3   3   1   3   3   ?

3 1   2   3   1   2   3   1   ?   **4** 5   4   2   5   4   2   5   4   ?

5 3   3   2   3   3   2   3   ?   **6** 1   1   5   5   5   1   1   ?

Example

Copy and finish the pattern.

3   3   1   1   3   3   1   1   ?   ?   ?   ?
└─────────────┘
              └─── this part repeats

Answer:

3   3   1   1   3   3   1   1   3   3   1   1
└──────────────────────────┘   └──────────┘
            copied   next 4 numbers

Exercise 2E

Copy and finish these patterns.

1   4   2   2   4   2   2   4   ?   ?

2   1   9   9   1   9   9   ?   ?   ?

3   6   4   6   4   6   4   ?   ?

4   3   3   5   5   3   3   5   5   ?   ?   ?   ?

5   8   4   4   8   4   4   8   4   4   ?   ?   ?

6   7   8   9   7   8   9   7   ?   ?

Example

Use 6s and 2s to make a repeating number pattern.

Answer: 6   2   6   2   6   2   or   6   2   2   6   2   2

  or   2   6   6   2   6   6

Make a pattern from 6s and 2s.

  6   2   *or*
6   2   2   *or*   2   6   6
Repeat it.

Exercise 2F

Use these numbers to make a repeating number pattern.

1   2s and 4s   **2**   3s and 1s

3   5s and 8s   **4**   3s and 6s

Remember
Look at the shapes or numbers to see the pattern.
Say the shapes or numbers to hear the pattern.

3 Up to 100

You already know the numbers up to 20.

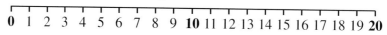

To count up to 100 you need to know all the numbers up to 100 in order.

The number line to 100 looks like this:

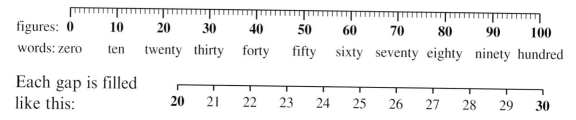

Each gap is filled like this:

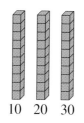

Counting in tens

Sometimes it is quicker to count in steps of 10.

Example

How many?

Answer: 30

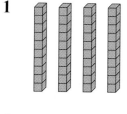

You could count all the cubes:
1,2,3,4,5,6,7,8,9,10...28,29,30
It is quicker to count in tens.

Exercise 3A

Count in tens. How many?

1

2

3
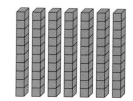

4
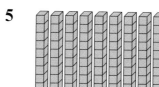

5

6

Example

What comes next?   10   20   30
Write it in words.

    10   20   30

Look at the number line. 40 comes next.

Answer: forty

Exercise 3B

What comes next? Write it in words.

1   10   20   30   40   50   **2**   50   60   70

3   20   30   40   **4**   30   40   50   60

5   40   50   60   70   **6**   60   70   80

7   70   80   90   **8**   70   80   90

Tens and units

You can use cubes to make numbers.

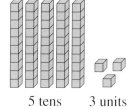

53 is

                5 tens   3 units

Example

How many? Write in figures and words.

Count the tens:

10 20 30

Count on the units:

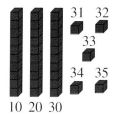

                                  31 32
                                    33
                                  34 35

10 20 30

Answer: 35, thirty five

Exercise 3C

How many? Write in figures and words.

1 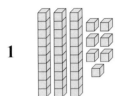   **2**    **3**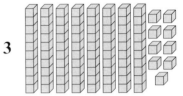

4    **5** 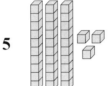   **6**   **7**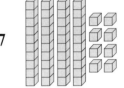

8 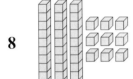   **9** 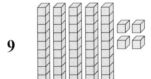   **10**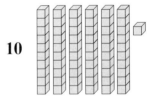

Example

Draw 57.

Make 50 in tens: Add 7 units: Answer: 57 is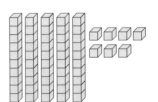

Exercise 3D

1 Draw:

    a 34   **b** 65   **c** 98   **d** 27   **e** 71

    f 29   **g** 17   **h** 55   **i** 43   **j** 84

2 Write in words:

    a 27   **b** 58   **c** 88   **d** 43   **e** 65   **f** 74

    g 91   **h** 32   **i** 56   **j** 93   **k** 81   **l** 48

3 Write in figures:

    a fifty one   **b** seventy four   **c** thirty seven   **d** ninety six

    e eighty three   **f** forty nine   **g** twenty two   **h** sixty three

4 Ordering

You have learnt the numbers up to 100 in **order**.
They get larger as you count along the number line.

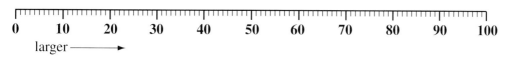

larger ⟶

Here are 2 packets of toffees.

Which would you choose?
You need to know which is largest: 75 or 56?

Look at the number line. 75 comes after 56, so 75 is largest.

Example

Which is smaller?   26   74

26 comes before 74, so 26 is smaller.

Answer: 26

Example

Which is larger?   44   94

94 comes after 44, so 94 is larger.

Answer: 94

Exercise 4A

1   Which is smaller?
   a 27 58   **b** 43 29   **c** 36 21   **d** 74 93
   e 63 82   **f** 14 23   **g** 17 71   **h** 53 39

2   Which is larger?
   a 91 72   **b** 61 34   **c** 91 33   **d** 51 60
   e 15 51   **f** 44 71   **g** 29 19   **h** 78 87

3   Which is smallest?
   a 41 72 37   **b** 91 82 87   **c** 17 81 52

4   Which is largest?
   a 53 27 44   **b** 78 36 25   **c** 19 81 94

5   Which is the largest number?   27 42 19 71 66

6   Which is the smallest number?   77 21 62 31 84

Writing numbers in order

|10| |20| |30| are in order, **smallest** first.

|2| |53| |84| are in order, **smallest** first.

|57| |45| |26| are in order, **largest** first.

|100| |75| |50| are in order, **largest** first.

Example

Write these numbers in order,

smallest first: |81| |27| |57|

Read all the numbers.

Which is smallest? |27|

Which is next smallest? |57|

Which is next smallest? |81|

Answer: |27| |57| |81|

Example

Write these numbers in order,

largest first: |18| |68| |86| |81|

Read all the numbers.

Which is largest? |86|

Next largest? |81|

Next largest? |68|

Next largest? |18|

Answer: |86| |81| |68| |18|

Exercise 4B

1   Write these numbers in order, smallest first:

  a |25| |37| |15| b |16| |11| |28| c |75| |34| |65| |19|

  d |84| |35| |52| |19| e |92| |89| |21| |12|

2   Write these numbers in order, largest first:

  a |62| |52| |79| b |38| |93| |88| c |26| |3| |88| |53|

  d |49| |29| |25| |27| e |56| |11| |58| |45|

Remember

Read the numbers to hear which is smallest.

Look at the number line.

5 Beyond 100

You write numbers up to 100 using tens and units.
This page shows you how to write numbers over 100.

100 is    which is

10 'towers' or 10 'tens'   100 block

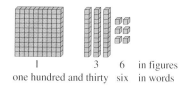

1   3   6   in figures
one hundred and thirty six   in words

Example

Write in figures
and words:

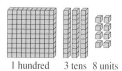

1 hundred   3 tens 8 units

Answer:
138, one hundred and thirty eight

Exercise 5A

Write in figures and words:

1   **2**   **3**   **4**

5   **6**   **7**   **8**

Example

Draw   143.   Answer:

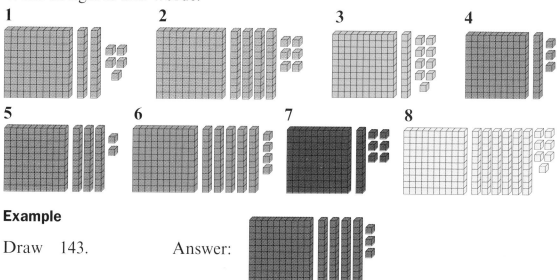

Exercise 5B

Draw:

1 129   **2** 173   **3** 146   **4** 129

5   Write in words:

  a 147   **b** 176   **c** 182   **d** 110   **e** 133   **f** 150   **g** 175   **h** 199

6 Counting in steps

You can already count in 10s or 'steps of 10'.
Sometimes you need to be able to count in other size steps.

Using a number line

If you're counting money in 2ps you need to count in steps of 2.

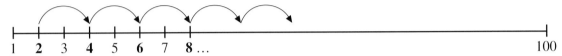

Start with 2 and count on in steps of 2. This gives the numbers 2, 4, 6, 8, 10 and so on.

Start with 1 and count on in steps of 2. This gives the numbers 1, 3, 5, 7 and so on.

Using fingers

Use your fingers to help count on like this:

Start with 3 and count on in steps of 4.
Hold up 4 fingers.

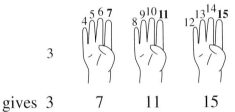

gives 3   7   11   15

> Remember to count from the same end each time.

Example

Count on from 4 in steps of 3.   4 — — — —

Use a number line or your fingers.

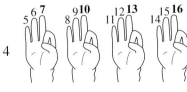

Answer: 4   7   10   13   16

Exercise 6A

1 Count on from 5 in steps of 2.

5 — — — —

2 Count on from 2 in steps of 3.

2 — — — —

3 Count on from 3 in steps of 2.

3 — — — —

4 Count on from 4 in steps of 2.

4 — — — —

5 Count on from 6 in steps of 4.

6 — — — —

Using the 100 square

The numbers 1 to 100 can be set out in a square like this. You can use the 100 square for counting 1, 2, 3, . . .
You can also use it for counting on in steps.
Using the square to start with 3 and count on in steps of 3 four times:

1	2	3	4	5	6	7	8	9	10
11	12	13	14	15	16	17	18	19	20
21	22	23	24	25	26	27	28	29	30
31	32	33	34	35	36	37	38	39	40
41	42	43	44	45	46	47	48	49	50
51	52	53	54	55	56	57	58	59	60
61	62	63	64	65	66	67	68	69	70
71	72	73	74	75	76	77	78	79	80
81	82	83	84	85	86	87	88	89	90
91	92	93	94	95	96	97	98	99	100

3 steps

Start

Now go to start of the next line.

Keep counting in steps as far as you need.

gives the numbers 3 6 9 12 15

Example

Use a 100 square to help you count on from 5 in steps of 3.

Answer: 5 8 11 14

Exercise 6B

Use a 100 square to help.

1   Count on from 4 in steps of 4.

      4   —   —   —   —

2   Count on from 5 in steps of 4.

      5   —   —   —   —

3   Count on from 8 in steps of 3.

      8   —   —   —   —

4   Count on from 13 in steps of 2.

      13   —   —   —   —

1	2	3	4	5	6	7	8	9	10
11	12	13	14	15	16	17	18	19	20
21	22	23	24	25	26	27	28	29	30
31	32	33	34	35	36	37	38	39	40
41	42	43	44	45	46	47	48	49	50
51	52	53	54	55	56	57	58	59	60
61	62	63	64	65	66	67	68	69	70
71	72	73	74	75	76	77	78	79	80
81	82	83	84	85	86	87	88	89	90
91	92	93	94	95	96	97	98	99	100

Starting from 7 and counting on in steps of 3 gives the numbers:
7, 10, 13, 16, 19, 22, 25, 28, 31, 34, ... (the numbers shaded).

Example

Count on from 15 in steps of 4.

      15   —   —   —   —   —

Answer: Use a 100 square:

      15   19   23   27   31   35

Exercise 6C

Give the first 6 numbers:

1   Count on from 20 in steps of 5.

2   Count on from 16 in steps of 2.

3   Count on from 9 in steps of 4.

4   Count on from 6 in steps of 5.

5   Count on from 12 in steps of 3.

6   Count on from 10 in steps of 4.

7   Count on from 22 in steps of 6.

8   Count on from 17 in steps of 3.

9   Count on from 14 in steps of 4.

10   Count on from 11 in steps of 5.

11   Count on from 13 in steps of 6.

12   Count on from 15 in steps of 2.

13   Count on from 8 in steps of 4.

14   Count on from 10 in steps of 5.

7 Measuring lines

You have already practised comparing measurements and sizes.

Example

Which line is longer?

——————————— A

A is 2 fingerwidths

Use your fingers to check:

——————————————— B

B is 3 fingerwidths

Answer: B is longer.

Using a ruler

Everyone's fingerwidths are different sizes. You can use a ruler to measure lengths in centimetres. Centimetres are the same size on **every** ruler.

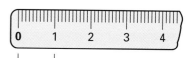

This is 1 centimetre
or 1 cm for short.

To answer a 'how long' question, measure with a ruler.

Example

How long is this line?

————————————————————————————————

1 Place the ruler so the ↓ line starts at 0.

2 Read the value off ↓ the ruler.

Answer: The line is 10 cm long.

Exercise 7A

How long are these lines?

1
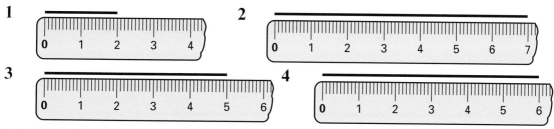

2

3

4

Measure these lines. Use a ruler.

5 ————————

6 ———————————————

7 ————————————

8   ——————————

Drawing lines

Example

Draw a line 6 cm long.

1 Start with your pencil at zero

2 Draw along the edge of the ruler. Stop when you get to 6.

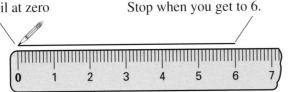

For a 'draw a line' question, use a ruler.

Answer: _____

Exercise 7B

Draw lines with these lengths.

1 4 cm   **2** 10 cm   **3** 7 cm   **4** 3 cm

Comparing lengths

To compare lengths you can measure them first.

Example

Measure each line. Which is longest?

A ——————————————

B ————————————————

C ——————————

A is 6 cm

B is 7 cm

C is 4 cm

The largest number of centimetres is the longest measurement.

Answer: B is longest.

Exercise 7C

Measure each line.

1 Which is shortest?   **2** Which is longest?

P ——————————————   W ————————

Q ————————   X ————————————————

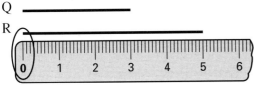

3 Which is longest?

P ————

Q —————

R ——————

4 Which is longest?

W ————————

X ———————

Y —————————

5 Which is longest? Which is shortest?

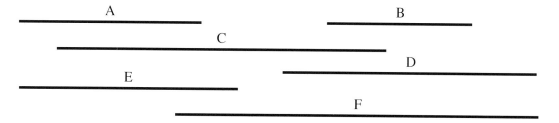

Measuring objects

You can measure objects with a ruler, the same way as you measure lines.

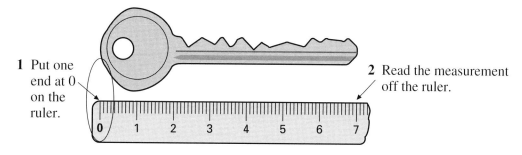

1 Put one end at 0 on the ruler.

2 Read the measurement off the ruler.

This key is 7 cm long.

Exercise 7D

1 Measure each pen.

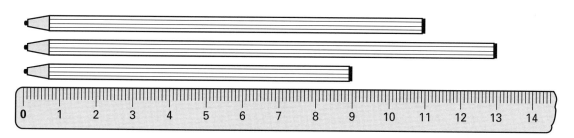

More measuring

Example

Which lines are 4 cm long?

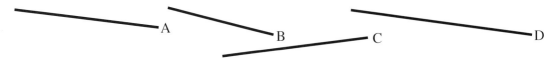

Use a ruler to measure all the lines: A 4 cm,   B 3 cm,   C 4 cm,   D 5 cm
Answer: A and C.

Exercise 7E

1   Which lines are 7 cm long?

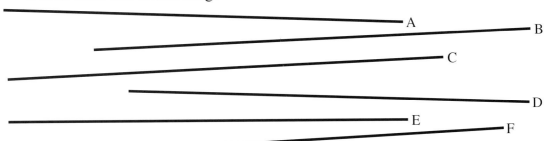

2   Which lines are 12 cm long?

3   Which lines are bigger than 8 cm?

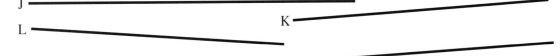

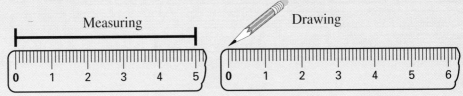

Remember   When you measure *or* draw, always start the line at 0 on the ruler.

Measuring

Drawing

8 Folding and shading

One way of splitting a shape in
half is by folding.
Fold a piece of paper like this:

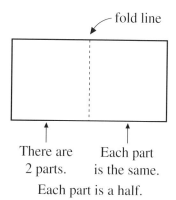

There are   Each part
2 parts.   is the same.

Each part is a half.

These shapes have been folded in half.
One half has been shaded:

In each shape the shaded and unshaded parts are the same.

Example

Which shapes have half shaded?

a    b   c

Look to see if both parts are the same.

This is
half ——→ 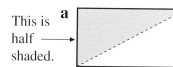   b   This is *not* half.
shaded.   The parts shaded
                                 and unshaded are
                                 not the same.

c 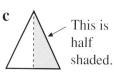 This is
                         half
                         shaded.

Answer: **a, c**

Exercise 8A

Which shapes have half shaded?

a   b   c   d   e

Splitting into 2 halves

Here is a chocolate bar.

For 2 people you can share it in 2 halves.

It can be broken in half like this:

Each person gets the same.

or like this:

or like this:

Count the squares of chocolate to make sure the shares are equal.

Here is another chocolate bar with half shaded.

1	4	1	4
2	5	2	5
3	6	3	6

Check by counting the shaded and unshaded squares.
There are six of each.

Example

Which chocolate bars have half shaded? Check by counting.

a

b (grid, top-left shaded)

c (grid, L-shape shaded)

a

This is half shaded.
There are 4 shaded
and 4 unshaded.

b

This is not half.
There are 2 shaded
and 6 unshaded.

c

This is half shaded.
There are 4 shaded
and 4 unshaded.

Answer: **a, c**

Exercise 8B

Which chocolate bars have half shaded?

a   b   c   d

e    f   g    h

Example

Which shapes have half shaded?

a   b   c

a   b   c

2 shaded	2 shaded	2 shaded
2 unshaded.	1 unshaded.	2 unshaded.
This is half shaded.	This not half.	This is half shaded.

Answer: **a, c**

> Check by counting shaded and unshaded parts. For half shaded, there must be equal numbers of shaded and unshaded parts.

Exercise 8C

Which shapes have half shaded?

a 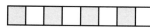   b

c   d   e   f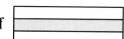

Remember
When you divide something in half, the 2 halves are **the same**.

9 Half of

To find half you divide into 2 equal parts.

You can find half of a number by folding a strip of squares

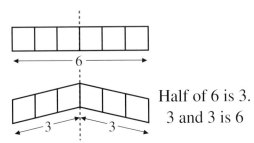

Half of 6 is 3.
3 and 3 is 6

or by using counters.

Count 10 counters.

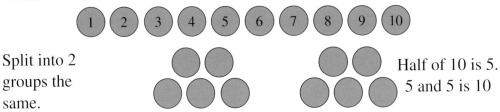

Split into 2 groups the same.

Half of 10 is 5.
5 and 5 is 10

Example

Work out half of 12.

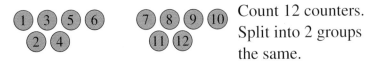

Count 12 counters.
Split into 2 groups
the same.

Answer: Half of 12 is 6.

Exercise 9A

1   Work out half of these numbers:
     a 8   **b** 2   **c** 4   **d** 10   **e** 16   **f** 14   **g** 18

2   Work out half of:
     a 20   **b** 30   **c** 28   **d** 24   **e** 26   **f** 32   **g** 22

Even and odd

<table>
<tr><td>

Even
If a number can be divided into
two halves, we say it is **even**.

</td><td>

Odd
Odd numbers can't be divided
into 2 halves.

</td></tr>
</table>

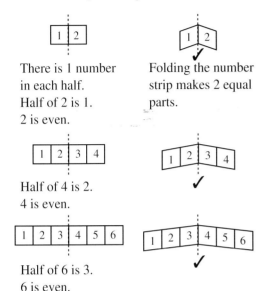

There is 1 number
in each half.
Half of 2 is 1.
2 is even.

Folding the number
strip makes 2 equal
parts.

Half of 4 is 2.
4 is even.

Half of 6 is 3.
6 is even.

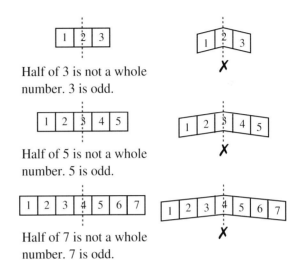

Half of 3 is not a whole
number. 3 is odd.

Half of 5 is not a whole
number. 5 is odd.

Half of 7 is not a whole
number. 7 is odd.

Exercise 9B

Use a 100 square.

1   Shade 2. Count on in steps of 2
    and shade each step.

    Write your numbers like this
    2, 4, 6, . . .
    These are the numbers that you
    can divide into two equal halves.

    The shaded numbers are *even*.

1	2	3	4	5	6	7	8	9	10
11	12	13	14	15	16	17	18	19	20
21	22	23	24	25	26	27	28	29	30
31	32	33	34	35	36	37	38	39	40
41	42	43	44	45	46	47	48	49	50
51	52	53	54	55	56	57	58	59	60
61	62	63	64	65	66	67	68	69	70
71	72	73	74	75	76	77	78	79	80
81	82	83	84	85	86	87	88	89	90
91	92	93	94	95	96	97	98	99	100

2   Write the unshaded numbers like this
    1, 3, 5, 7, 9, 11, 13, . . .

    The unshaded numbers are *odd*.

The even numbers always end in 2, 4, 6, 8, 0.

The odd numbers always end in 1, 3, 5, 7, 9.

Example

Write down the odd numbers from this list:

    84   27   52   45   18   8

Answer: 2<u>7</u>   4<u>5</u>   because they end in 7 and 5, 7 and 5 are odd.

Exercise 9C

1   Write down the even numbers from this list:

    92, 47, 36, 38, 51, 19, 2, 88

2   Write down the odd numbers from this list:

    23, 11, 42, 98, 79, 64, 49

3   Write down the even numbers from this list:

    11, 22, 33, 44, 55, 66, 77, 88

4   Write down the odd numbers from this list:

    2, 73, 18, 15, 19, 47, 52, 80

5   Write down the even numbers from this list:

    10, 73, 83, 38, 37, 92, 45

6   Write down the odd numbers from this list:

    91, 76, 43, 57, 60, 42, 13

Remember

Even numbers can be divided into halves.
Odd numbers can't be divided into halves.

The even numbers are:

2, 4, 6, 8, 10, 12, 14, 16, 18, 20, ...

They always end in 0, 2, 4, 6, 8.

The odd numbers are:

1, 3, 5, 7, 9, 11, 13, 15, 17, 19, 21 ...

They always end in 1, 3, 5, 7, 9.

10 Angles 1

Here is a spinner.

The spinner has turned.

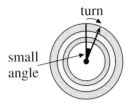

turn

small angle

The distance it turns is called the **angle**.

The spinner has turned some more

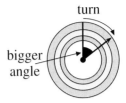

turn

bigger angle

The angle is now **bigger**.

You use angles to measure turns.

Here is another spinner.
It turns the other way.

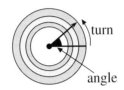

turn

angle

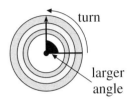

turn

larger angle

Example

Which angle is larger, A or B?
A has turned more than B.

Answer: A is larger.

A

B

Exercise 10A

1 Which angle is smaller?

A   B

2 Which angle is larger?

A   B

3 Which angle is larger?

A   B

4 Which angle is smaller?

A   B

5 Which angle is larger?

A   B

6 Which angle is smaller?

A   B

These are the angles a spinner has turned. The spinner has not been drawn.

Example

Which angle is bigger?

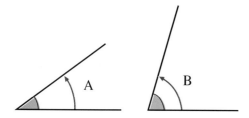

B is a bigger turn than A.

Answer: B

Example

Which is the smaller angle?

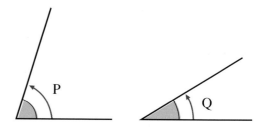

Q is a smaller turn than P.

Answer: Q

Exercise 10B

1   Which angle is bigger?

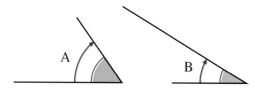

2   Which angle is smaller?

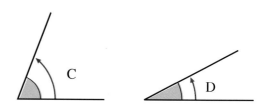

3   Which angle is larger?

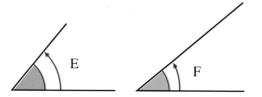

4   Which is the bigger angle?

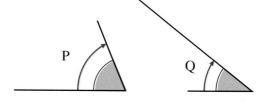

5   Which is the smaller angle?

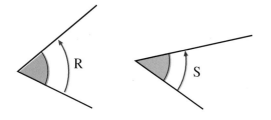

6   Which angle is smaller?

Example

Which angle is smallest?

Q is the smallest turn.

Answer: Q

 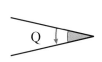 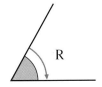

Exercise 10C

1 Which angle is smallest?

 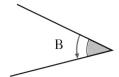 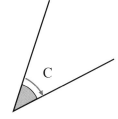

2 Which angle is largest?

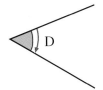 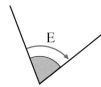 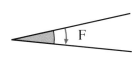

3 Which angle is biggest? Which angle is smallest?

  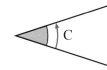

4 Which is the biggest angle? Which is the smallest angle?

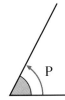 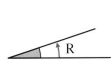

Remember
Angles measure turns and turning.
The bigger the turn, the bigger the angle.
The smaller the turn, the smaller the angle.

11 More shading

On page 57 you saw how to split a shape in half. This page will show you how to split a shape into quarters.

Fold a sheet of paper like this: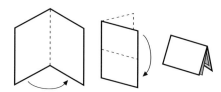

quarter	quarter
quarter	quarter

There are 4 parts. Each part is the *same*. Each part is a **quarter**.

These shapes have been folded in quarters and one quarter shaded.

 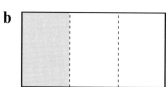 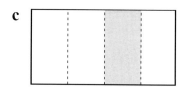

They each have 4 parts the same and one part shaded.

Example

Which shapes have a quarter shaded?

a   b   c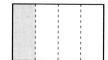

Look to see how many parts there are.

a 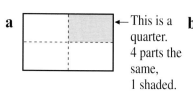 ← This is a quarter. 4 parts the same, 1 shaded.

b 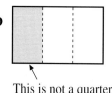 This is not a quarter. Not 4 parts.

c 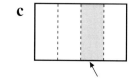 This is a quarter. 4 parts the same, 1 shaded.

Answer: **a, c**

Exercise 11A

Which shapes have a quarter shaded?

a   b  c

d 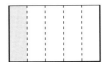 e

Splitting into 4 quarters

Here is a chocolate bar.
For 4 people you can share it into 4 quarters.

It can be broken into quarters like this:

Each person gets the same.

Here is another chocolate bar with a quarter shaded.

There are 4 pieces the same:

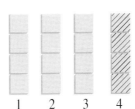

Example

Which chocolate bars have a quarter shaded?

a

b

c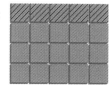

Look to see which have 4 parts the same.

a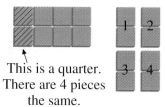

This is a quarter.
There are 4 pieces
the same.

b

This is not a quarter.
There are not 4 pieces of [ ] [ ] [ ] .

c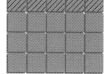

This is a quarter.
There are 4 pieces the same:

Answer: **a, c**

Exercise 11B

Which chocolate bars have a quarter shaded?

a

b

c

d

e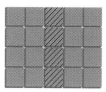

f

g

h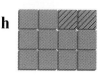

Example

Which shape has a quarter shaded? **a** 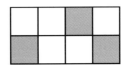 **b**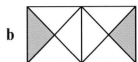

Answer: **a** This is not a quarter. There are not 4 lots of

b This is a quarter. There are 4 lots of

Exercise 11C

Which shapes have a quarter shaded?

1   **2**   **3**   **4**

5 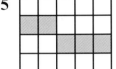 **6**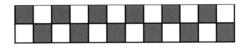

7   **8**   **9**   **10**

11  **12**   **13**   **14**

15   **16**   **17**   **18**

Remember
When you divide something into quarters you make **4** equal parts.
The 4 quarters are the *same*.

12 Adding and subtracting

You have already learnt how to add two sets of objects together or take some away to find out how many are left.

These exercises give you some more practice.

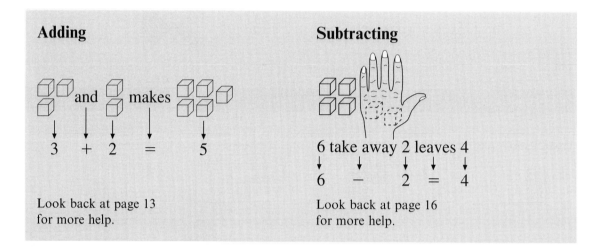

Adding

$$3 + 2 = 5$$

Look back at page 13 for more help.

Subtracting

6 take away 2 leaves 4

$$6 - 2 = 4$$

Look back at page 16 for more help.

Example

Work out $5 + 4$

Use cubes:

Answer: $5 + 4 = 9$

Exercise 12A

Work out these. Use cubes to help.

a $1 + 3$ b $2 + 5$ c $7 + 2$ d $6 + 4$ e $4 + 2$ f $8 + 1$
g $3 + 5$ h $2 + 8$ i $4 + 3$ j $5 + 1$ k $7 + 1$ l $5 + 5$

Example

Work out $7 - 4$
Use cubes:

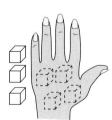

Cover 4.

Answer: $7 - 4 = 3$

Exercise 12B

Work out these. Use cubes to help.

1 **a** $4-1$ **b** $7-2$ **c** $8-3$ **d** $9-5$ **e** $6-4$ **f** $10-2$
   g $9-6$ **h** $7-6$ **i** $10-4$ **j** $5-2$ **k** $8-6$ **l** $10-7$

2 **a** $4+3$ **b** $7-3$ **c** $6+2$ **d** $8-2$ **e** $10-5$ **f** $4+1$
   g $6-1$ **h** $2+2$ **i** $7+3$ **j** $4+5$ **k** $10-3$ **l** $9-7$

Using a number line

This is another way of working out addition or subtraction sums.

Example   **Example**

Addition $5+4$ **Subtraction $7-4$**

Start on 5.   Start on 7.
Count on 4 steps to get to 9.   Count back 4 steps to get to 3.

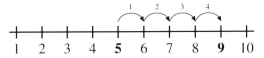   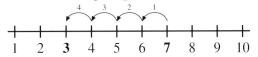

Answer: $5+4=9$ Answer: $7-4=3$

Exercise 12C

Use a number line to work these out.

1 **a** $6+2$ **b** $4+3$ **c** $7+2$ **d** $2+8$
   e $1+7$ **f** $3+2$ **g** $9+1$ **h** $3+5$
   i $4+5$ **j** $5+2$ **k** $2+3$ **l** $4+4$

2 **a** $9-2$ **b** $6-3$ **c** $5-2$ **d** $8-5$
   e $7-3$ **f** $9-4$ **g** $3-2$ **h** $6-2$
   i $5-4$ **j** $8-3$ **k** $7-2$ **l** $6-4$

3 **a** $4+2$ **b** $8-2$ **c** $5+3$ **d** $10-3$
   e $2+6$ **f** $9-5$ **g** $7-5$ **h** $5+5$
   i $8-4$ **j** $3+6$ **k** $8+2$ **l** $10-4$

Remember   When you use a number line, **count on** to **add on**
                                              count back to **take away**.

13 Sort it

You can sort objects into sets by their important features.

Here is a tile.

A B 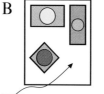 C

The tile goes in set B.

They all have 4 straight sides and a circle inside.

Example

Does go in A, B or C?   A B C

Look for shapes in the sets with the same features.

goes in B because the shapes are solid and they are the same at both ends.

Answer: B

Exercise 13A

1   Does go in A, B or C?

A B 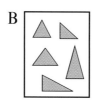 C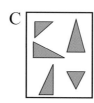

2   Does  go in A, B or C?

A  B  C

3 Where does the  belong: A, B or C?

A   B   C

4 Does go in A, B or C?

A   B   C

5 Does (20p) go in A, B or C?

A   B   C

6 Does 2 go in A, B or C?

A
4	6
	8	6
8	4

B
12	18
	14	
16	12
	18	

C
	5
3	
	5	7
7	9

7 Does 10 go in A, B or C?

A
12	14
	18	16
16	14

B
11	13
	15	
11	17
	19	

C
	3
1	
	5	7
3	9

8 Where does A belong?

A
a	
	f	
	t
g	

B
C	D
	R	
J	S

C
E	
	F	T
Z	N
	M

9 Where does belong?•

A   B   C

14 Making 10

There are several ways of making 10.
Here are some of them:

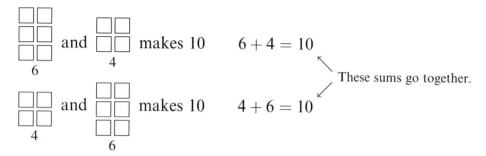

You can split 10 cubes into two groups and write two sums like this:

8 + 2 = 10 and 2 + 8 = 10

Example

Copy and complete: $6 + 4 = 10$

$4 + \boxed{} = 10$

The sums go together.
Look at the first sum to see which number is missing in
the second sum.

Answer: $4 + \boxed{6} = 10$

Exercise 14A

Copy and complete:

1 $7 + 3 = 10$

$3 + \boxed{} = 10$

2 $9 + 1 = 10$

$1 + \boxed{} = 10$

3 $5 + 5 = 10$

$5 + \boxed{} = 10$

4 $8 + 2 = 10$

$2 + \boxed{} = 10$

Example

Copy and complete: $7 + \boxed{} = 10$

Use 10 cubes:

Count 7 →

3 are left

Answer: $7 + \boxed{3} = 10$

Exercise 14B ◦

Use 10 cubes. Copy and complete:

1 **a** $1 + \boxed{} = 10$ **b** $5 + \boxed{} = 10$ **c** $8 + \boxed{} = 10$

2 **a** $9 + \boxed{} = 10$ **b** $\boxed{} + 2 = 10$ **c** $3 + \boxed{} = 10$

3 **a** $\boxed{} + 5 = 10$ **b** $6 + \boxed{} = 10$ **c** $\boxed{} + 4 = 10$

Using a number line

Instead of cubes you can use a number line to work out the missing numbers.

$8 + \boxed{} = 10$

Start on 8.
Count on 2 steps to get to 10.

so $8 + \boxed{2} = 10$

The same method works for subtraction.
$10 - \boxed{} = 8$

Start on 10.
Go back 2 steps to get to 8.

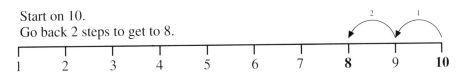

so $10 - \boxed{2} = 8$

$8 + 2 = 10$ and $10 - 2 = 8$ go together.

Example

$7 + 3 = 10$ and $10 - \square = 7$ go together.

Start on 7.
Count on 3 steps to get to 10.

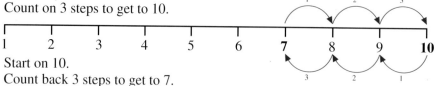

Start on 10.
Count back 3 steps to get to 7.

Answer: $7 + 3 = 10$ and $10 - 3 = 7$ go together.

Exercise 14C

1 Copy and complete:

   a $1 + 9 = 10$ **b** $6 + 4 = 10$ **c** $2 + 8 = 10$
        $10 - \square = 1$ $10 - \square = 6$ $10 - \square = 2$

2 Use the number line. Copy and complete:

   a $10 - \square = 4$ **b** $10 - \square = 9$ **c** $10 - \square = 4$
   d $10 - \square = 5$ **e** $10 - \square = 3$ **f** $10 - \square = 7$
   g $10 - \square = 2$

3 Copy and complete these patterns:

   a $1 + 9 = 10$ **b** $10 - 9 = 1$
        $2 + 8 = 10$ $10 - 8 = 2$
        $3 + 7 = 10$ $10 - 7 = 3$
        $4 + 6 = \square$ $10 - 6 = 4$
        $5 + \square = 10$ $10 - \square = 5$
        $\square + 4 = 10$ $10 - 4 = \square$
        $7 + 3 = 10$ $\square - 3 = 7$
        $8 + \square = 10$ $10 - \square = \square$
        $\square + \square = 10$ $\square - \square = 9$

What do you notice?

15 Using a calculator

You can use a calculator to add (+) and subtract (−).

Addition

To work out   24 + 58

press $\boxed{2}\boxed{4}\boxed{+}\boxed{5}\boxed{8}\boxed{=}$

giving $\boxed{\textit{82.}}$

so   24 + 58 = 82

Example

Work out 56 + 47

Press $\boxed{5}\boxed{6}\boxed{+}\boxed{4}\boxed{7}\boxed{=}$ giving $\boxed{\textit{103.}}$

Answer: 103

Exercise 15A

Use a calculator to work out:

1 **a** 54 + 27 **b** 63 + 39 **c** 77 + 92
   d 52 + 38 **e** 91 + 47 **f** 65 + 82

2 **a** 67 + 43 **b** 81 + 18 **c** 49 + 16
   d 84 + 19 **e** 73 + 56 **f** 71 + 28

3 **a** 88 + 55 **b** 75 + 48 **c** 57 + 34
   d 94 + 14 **e** 76 + 29 **f** 104 + 29

Subtraction

To work out   73 − 25

press $\boxed{7}\boxed{3}\boxed{-}\boxed{2}\boxed{5}\boxed{=}$

giving $\boxed{\textit{48.}}$

so   73 − 25 = 48

Example

Work out 48 − 29

Press $\boxed{4}\boxed{8}\boxed{-}\boxed{2}\boxed{9}\boxed{=}$ giving $\boxed{19.}$

Answer: 19

Exercise 15B

Use a calculator to work out:

1 a 62 − 49   b 57 − 28   c 92 − 77
   d 58 − 39   e 342 − 154   f 198 − 57

2 a 81 − 37   b 43 − 37   c 63 − 36
   d 62 − 25   e 104 − 89   f 105 − 98

3 a 70 − 15   b 100 − 11   c 150 − 1
   d 242 − 158   e 71 − 12   f 726 − 193

Problems using addition

Some questions are written in words. You need to find the sum to do and work out the answer.

Example

There are 22 people in a room, 15 more join them. How many are there altogether?

The sum is 22 add 15.

$\boxed{2}\boxed{2}\boxed{+}\boxed{1}\boxed{5}\boxed{=}$ gives $\boxed{37.}$

Answer: 37 people

Exercise 15C

Use a calculator for these.

1   There are 24 books on a shelf in a library,
    then 17 more are added.
    How many books are on the shelf altogether?

2   A teacher put 35 cubes in a box, the pupils
    add another 27.
    How many cubes are in the box altogether?

3   The canteen sells 45 colas in the morning
    and 52 colas at lunch time.
    How many colas did the canteen sell altogether?

Problems using subtraction

First find the sum to do. Then work out the answer.

Example

56 paper clips are taken from a box of 144 paper clips.
How many are left?

$\boxed{1}\boxed{4}\boxed{4}\boxed{-}\boxed{5}\boxed{6}\boxed{=}$ gives $\boxed{88.}$

Answer: 88 paper clips

Exercise 15D

1   Amil has 48 football cards. He gives 25 to his brother.
    How many does he have left?

2   There are 52 chocolate bars in a machine,
    35 are bought at lunchtime.
    How many are left?

3   There are 38 people on a bus, 29 get off at the next stop.
    How many are left?

More practice

For these questions, first decide if it is an addition or a
subtraction. Write down the sum. Use a calculator to
work out the answer.

Exercise 15E

1   There are 23 cars in a car park, then another 48 go in.
    How many cars are in the park?

2   There are 65 newspapers in a pile, 38 are sold.
    How many newspapers are left?

3   150 sheets of paper are put into a printer, 84 sheets are used.
    How many sheets are left?

4   There are 100 cubes in a box, James takes 35.
    How many are left in the box?

5   There are 84 spoons in a tub, 45 are used.
    How many spoons are left in the tub?

6   A video shop has 24 cartoon tapes on the shelf and another
    68 out on rent.
    How many cartoon tapes has the shop altogether?

Remember

The words in the problem tell you what kind of sum it is.

'How many are left?' This means some have gone.
It is a **subtraction** sum.

'How many altogether?' This means some have been
added. It is an **addition** sum.

16 Measuring

This is how you work out the distance around a shape.

Here is a rectangle:

Here is an L-shape:

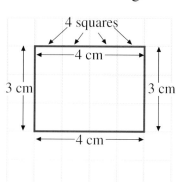

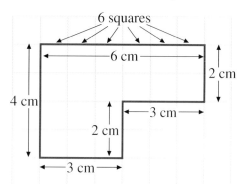

Count the squares along each side. The side of each square represents 1 cm. Add the lengths of the sides together.

The distance all the way around is:

$4 + 3 + 4 + 3 = 14$ cm

The distance all the way around is:

$6 + 2 + 3 + 2 + 3 + 4 = 20$ cm

You can use a calculator to add the lengths together.

Exercise 16A

Work out the distance all around these shapes.

The side of each square represents 1 cm.

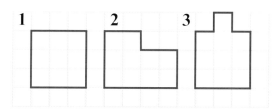

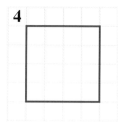

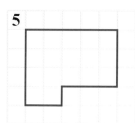

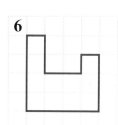

Sometimes the shapes have been measured for you.

Example

These shapes are not drawn life size.

Find the distance around
this shape.

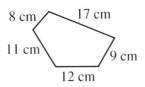

The measurements are all in cm.

$8 + 17 + 9 + 12 + 11$

$= 57\,\text{cm}$

Answer: 57 cm

Exercise 16B

Find the distance all the way around each shape.

1

4 cm   4 cm

4 cm

2

6 cm

4 cm   4 cm

6 cm

3

3 cm   4 cm

4 cm   5 cm

2 cm

4

3 cm

6 cm   6 cm

3 cm

5

2 cm

8 cm   5 cm

4 cm   3 cm

6 cm

6

5 cm

5 cm

All sides
are 5 cm

Measuring larger shapes

1 cm is quite a small measurement.

To measure large objects you use **metres**.

Your classroom is probably about 3 metres high.
You write **3 m**.

A man is nearly 2 metres tall.
You write **2 m**.

Example

Here is a plan of a carpet.
The sides have been measured in metres.
Find the distance around this carpet.

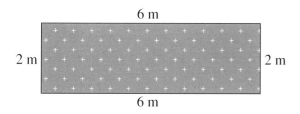

The distance around it is

$$6 + 2 + 6 + 2 = 16\,\text{m}$$

Answer: 16 m

Exercise 16C

Find the distance all the way around these:

1

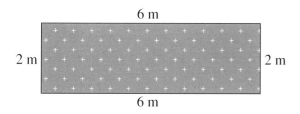

Play park — 10 m, 6 m, 6 metres

2

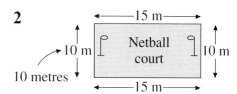

Netball court — 15 m, 10 m, 10 metres

3

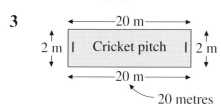

Cricket pitch — 20 m, 2 m, 20 metres

4

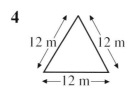

12 m, 12 m, 12 m

5

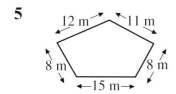

12 m, 11 m, 8 m, 8 m, 15 m

6

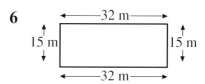

32 m, 15 m, 15 m, 32 m

Remember

When the measurements are in centimetres (cm) the answer must be in cm.

When the measurements are in metres (m) the answer must be in m.

17 Tables

Sometimes information is given in tables. This page
shows you how to read information from tables and how
to write information in a table.

This table shows the number of pupils in Class 10B at
school each day.

Class 10B	
Day	Number at school
Monday	26
Tuesday	28
Wednesday	28
Thursday	27
Friday	21

There were 26 pupils on Monday.

Tuesday and Wednesday had the same number.

Friday had the least.

Example

The table shows crisps sold.

Crisps	
Flavour	Packets
Ready salted	3
Cheese	5
Bacon	8
Chicken	4
Beef	2

a How many packets of cheese were sold?
b Which flavour sold least?
c Which flavour sold most?
d How many packets were sold altogether?

Crisps	
Flavour	Packets
Ready salted	3
Cheese	5
Bacon	8
Chicken	4
Beef	2

Answer:
a 5 packets of cheese were sold.

b Beef sold least.

c Bacon sold most.
d $3 + 5 + 8 + 4 + 2 = 22$
22 packets were sold altogether.

Remember

To answer questions like 'Which ... **least**?' Look for smallest number.

'Which ... **most**?' Look for largest number.

'How many...**altogether**?' Add the numbers to find the total.

Exercise 17A

1   The table shows the number of videos rented each day.

Day	Videos
Monday	52
Tuesday	67
Wednesday	32
Thursday	41
Friday	84
Saturday	95
Sunday	83

a   How many videos were rented on Tuesday?

b   When were most videos rented?

c   What was the least number of videos rented?

d   How many videos were rented on Thursday?

2   The table shows the attendance at a Sports Centre.

Day	Attendance
Monday	78
Tuesday	54
Wednesday	38
Thursday	42
Friday	57
Saturday	85
Sunday	94

a   How many people went on Tuesday?

b   How many people went on Saturday?

c   Which day had the largest attendance?

d   Which day had the smallest attendance?

3   The table shows activities of the pupils of Class 10B last night.

Activities	Number
Watch TV	4
Homework	8
Computer	2
Sports	7
Club	3

a   How many watched TV?

b   How many went out to sports or a club?

c   Which activity did most do?

d   How many pupils are there in the class?

Filling in a table

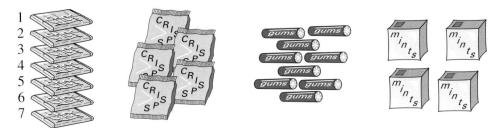

This table shows the number of choc bars, crisps, gums
and mints in a machine.

Items	Number	
Choc bars	7	There are 7 choc bars.
Crisps	5	There are 5 packets of crisps.
Gums	9	There are 9 packets of gums.
Mints	4	There are 4 boxes of mints.

Exercise 17B

1 Copy and complete the table for the
number of biscuits.

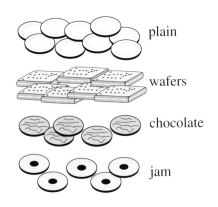

plain

wafers

chocolate

jam

Biscuits	Number
Plain	
Wafer	
Chocolate	
Jam	

2 Copy and complete the table for Class 11C.

Class 11C	Number at school
Monday	31
Tuesday	
Wednesday	
Thursday	
Friday	

a On Tuesday 27 pupils
were present at school.

b Wednesday and Thursday
had the same, 29 at
school.

c On Friday, there was one
more than Monday.

18 Collecting data

You can already read and fill in tables. On these pages
you will learn more ways of presenting information.

The information collected is called **data**.

Here is a list of the colours of the cars in a car park.

Blue	Yellow	Black	Red
Green	Black	Blue	Yellow
Red	Red	Green	Black
Black	Red	Blue	Black
Red	Red	Green	Green.

There are 20 cars altogether.

Copy this record sheet.

Colour	Tally	Number

Fill in your record sheet like this:

List the
different
car
colours

Colour	Tally	Number
Red	|	
Blue	|	
Yellow	|	
Green		
Black	|	

The first car is blue
Draw | for each car.
| is called a tally.
The next car is yellow.
The next car is black.

This shows the cars in the
first row of the list.

Continue filling in your record sheet for each row.
When you reach a tally of 5 draw the 5th tally across the
other 4 like this: ⊮

Your record sheet should look like this when you've
finished:

Colour	Tally	Number
Red	⊮ |	6 ←
Blue	|||	3
Yellow	||	2
Green	||||	4
Black	⊮	5

This is the number
of tallies for red cars.
$5 + 1 = 6$

Total 20 ← Check this total is the
same as the number
of cars in the list.

Example

Copy and complete the record sheet
to show the data. These are the number
of goals scored by a football team.

0	2	1	4	3	1	2	4	1
3	5	1	1	0	2	1	4	2
0	0	1	2	1	1	3	2	1

Goals	Tally	Number
0		
1		
2		
3		
4		
5		

Answer:

Goals	Tally	Number
0	||||	4
1	⊮ ⊮ ←	10
2	⊮ |	6
3	|||	3
4	|||	3
5	|	1

Count up in 5s say '5, 10'.

Exercise 18A

1 Copy and complete the record sheet to show the data.

In a game of monopoly these are the scores on the dice.

4 7 11 9 6 7 5 3 5 7
8 7 7 6 4 7 4 7 9 10
7 9 7 7 6 8 9 7 10 7

Score	Tally	Number
3		
4		
5		
6		
7		
8		
9		
10		
11		

2 Zara asked 20 people what was their favourite food. Here are the replies:

Chips   Ice Cream   Pizza   Pizza   Chicken
Salad   Chips   Chips   Ice Cream   Chips
Chips   Chicken   Chips   Chicken   Chips
Chips   Salad   Pizza   Chips   Chips

Copy and complete Zara's record sheet to show the data.

Food	Tally	Number
Chips		
Salad		
Ice Cream		
Chicken		
Pizza		

3 These are the hours of sunshine recorded one month.

5 4 7 6 9 9 8 10 10 7
9 10 9 10 9 7 8 4 6 5
7 8 10 8 6 3 6 8 3 3

Copy and complete the record to show the data.

Hours	Tally	Number
3		
4		
5		
6		
7		
8		
9		
10		

19 Block graphs

A block graph shows data as a diagram.

Example

From the record sheet for the cars on page 88 you can draw a block graph to show the data.

Colour	Tally	Number
Red	⊦⊦⊦⊦ |	6
Blue	|||	3
Yellow	||	2
Green	||||	4
Black	⊦⊦⊦⊦	5

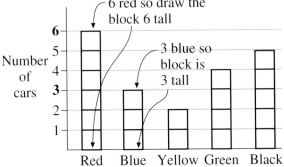

Exercise 19A

You will need squared paper.

1   This is Peter's record sheet.
    Copy and complete the block graph
    (on squared paper) to show the data.

Suit	Tally	Number
♡	⊦⊦⊦⊦ ⊦⊦⊦⊦ |	11
♣	⊦⊦⊦⊦ ||	7
♢	⊦⊦⊦⊦ ⊦⊦⊦⊦ ||	12
♤	⊦⊦⊦⊦	5

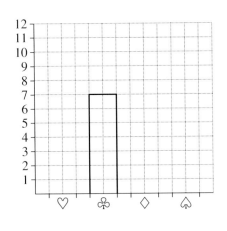

2   Marcos recorded the birds that visited his window sill for breadcrumbs.
    Copy and complete the block graph to show the data.

Bird	Tally	Number
Pigeon	⊦⊦⊦⊦ ||||	9
Sparrow	⊦⊦⊦⊦ |	6
Blackbird	||	2
Robin	|	1
Blue tit	|||	3

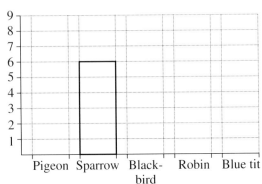

Reading graphs

Sometimes you are given a block graph and asked for information from it.

Example

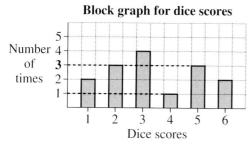

Block graph for dice scores

a How many times did the dice score 5?

b How many times did the dice score 4?

This means the dice scored 5 on 3 occasions.

a Find the block for 5. It is **3** tall.

b Find the block for 4. It is **1** tall.

Answer: 3 times

Answer: 1 time

Exercise 19B

1

Favourite sports

a How many people like football?

b How many people like tennis?

c How many people like hockey?

2

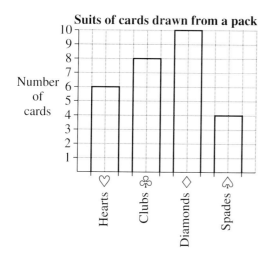

Suits of cards drawn from a pack

a How many times were diamonds drawn?

b How many times were hearts drawn?

c How many times were spades drawn?

Pictograms

Another way of showing information is a pictogram.
This is a pictogram for the cars record sheet.

Colour	Tally	Number
Red	IIII I	6
Blue	III	3
Yellow	II	2
Green	IIII	4
Black	IIII	5

6 red cars →

2 yellow cars →

Red	
Blue	
Yellow	
Green	
Black	

This is a **key**. The 🚗 is 1 car.

Exercise 19C

1 Nisha collected these results.
   Copy and complete the pictogram.

Dice score	Tally	Number
1	IIII I	6
2	III	3
3	IIII	4
4	III	3
5	III	3
6	II	2

1	
2	👤👤👤
3	
4	
5	
6	

Key: 👤 = 1 person

Sometimes you are given a pictogram and asked questions about it.

Example

Pictogram for drinks sold

Orange	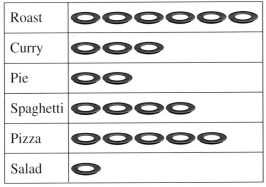
Apple	
Cola	
Milk	

Key: ⬜ = 1 drink

a How many milk drinks were sold?

b How many apple drinks were sold?

a 3 cups are shown for milk.
Answer: 3

b 2 cups are shown for apple.
Answer: 2

Exercise 19D

1   **Travel to work**

Bus	🧍🧍🧍🧍🧍🧍
Car	🧍🧍
Walk	🧍🧍🧍
Cycle	🧍🧍🧍🧍

Key: 🧍 = 1 person

a How many people travel by bus?

b How many people cycle?

c How many people walk?

2   **Favourite dinners**

Roast	⬭⬭⬭⬭⬭⬭
Curry	⬭⬭⬭
Pie	⬭⬭
Spaghetti	⬭⬭⬭⬭
Pizza	⬭⬭⬭⬭⬭
Salad	⬭

Key: ⬭ = 1 person

a How many people like pizza?

b How many people like roast?

c How many people like spaghetti?

d How many people like salad?

Remember   Tally marks are drawn in groups of 5: ⅲⅱ

Practice counting in 5's so you can count them quickly:

ⅲⅱ	ⅲⅱ ⅲⅱ	ⅲⅱ ⅲⅱ ⅲⅱ	ⅲⅱ ⅲⅱ ⅲⅱ ⅲⅱ	
5	10	15	20	and so on.

20 Addition and subtraction patterns

There are patterns in sums. If you find the pattern you can work out the next sum.

$$\text{go up in 1s} \begin{bmatrix} 0 + 1 = 1 \\ 1 + 1 = 2 \\ 2 + 1 = 3 \end{bmatrix} \text{go up in 1s}$$

$$\uparrow$$
stay the same

so the next line is $3 + 1 = 4$

$$\text{stay the same} \begin{bmatrix} 5 - 5 = 0 \\ 5 - 4 = 1 \\ 5 - 3 = 2 \\ 5 - 2 = 3 \end{bmatrix} \text{go up in 1s}$$

$$\uparrow$$
go down in 1s

so the next line is $5 - 1 = 4$

Example

Copy and complete:

$8 - 8 = 0$
$8 - 7 = 1$
$8 - \Box = 2$
$8 - \Box = \Box$
$\Box - \Box = \Box$
$\Box - \Box = \Box$
$\Box - \Box = \Box$
$\Box - \Box = \Box$

Answer:

stays goes goes
the   down up in
same in 1s   1s
↓   ↓   ↓

$8 - 8 = 0$
$8 - 7 = 1$
$8 - \boxed{6} = 2$
$8 - \boxed{5} = \boxed{3}$
$\boxed{8} - \boxed{4} = \boxed{4}$
$\boxed{8} - \boxed{3} = \boxed{5}$
$\boxed{8} - \boxed{2} = \boxed{6}$
$\boxed{8} - \boxed{1} = \boxed{7}$

Look for the **pattern**.

Example

Copy and complete:

$0 + 2 = 2$
$1 + 2 = 3$
$2 + 2 = 4$
$3 + \boxed{} = 5$
$\boxed{} + \boxed{} = 6$
$\boxed{} + \boxed{} = \boxed{}$
$\boxed{} + \boxed{} = \boxed{}$
$\boxed{} + \boxed{} = \boxed{}$

Answer:

goes up in 1s	stays the same	goes up in 1s
↓	↓	↓

$0 + 2 = 2$
$1 + 2 = 3$
$2 + 2 = 4$
$3 + \boxed{2} = 5$
$\boxed{4} + \boxed{2} = 6$
$\boxed{5} + \boxed{2} = \boxed{7}$
$\boxed{6} + \boxed{2} = \boxed{8}$
$\boxed{7} + \boxed{2} = \boxed{9}$

Exercise 20A

Copy and complete these patterns.

1

a
$4 - 4 = 0$
$4 - 3 = \boxed{}$
$4 - \boxed{} = 2$
$\boxed{} - \boxed{} = \boxed{}$

b
$3 - 0 = 3$
$3 - 1 = 2$
$\boxed{} - 2 = \boxed{}$
$\boxed{} - \boxed{} = \boxed{}$

c
$0 + 7 = 7$
$1 + 7 = 8$
$\boxed{} + 7 = 9$
$\boxed{} + \boxed{} = \boxed{}$

d
$7 - 7 = 0$
$7 - 6 = \boxed{}$
$7 - \boxed{} = 2$
$\boxed{} - \boxed{} = 3$
$\boxed{} - 3 = \boxed{}$
$\boxed{} - \boxed{} = \boxed{}$

e
$0 + 3 = 3$
$1 + 3 = \boxed{}$
$2 + \boxed{} = 5$
$\boxed{} + \boxed{} = \boxed{}$
$\boxed{} + \boxed{} = \boxed{}$

f
$0 + 6 = 6$
$1 + 6 = \boxed{}$
$2 + \boxed{} = 8$
$\boxed{} + \boxed{} = \boxed{}$
$\boxed{} + \boxed{} = \boxed{}$

g
$0 + 5 = 5$
$1 + 5 = 6$
$\boxed{} + \boxed{} = 7$
$\boxed{} + 5 = 8$
$\boxed{} + \boxed{} = 9$

h
$9 - 9 = 0$
$9 - 8 = 1$
$\boxed{} - 7 = 2$
$9 - \boxed{} = 3$
$\boxed{} - \boxed{} = \boxed{}$
$\boxed{} - \boxed{} = \boxed{}$

i
$6 - 6 = 0$
$6 - 5 = \boxed{}$
$6 - 4 = \boxed{}$
$\boxed{} - 3 = \boxed{}$
$\boxed{} - \boxed{} = \boxed{}$
$\boxed{} - \boxed{} = \boxed{}$

Number squares

Here is a number square for addition (+).

+	0	1	2	③	4
0	0	1	2	3	4
1	1	2	3	4	5
②	2	3	4	⑤	6
3	3	4	5	6	7
4	4	5	6	7	8

This shows $2 + 3 = 5$

Example

Complete the number square:

$0 + 2 =$

+	2	3	4
0	**2**	3	**4**
1	3	**4**	5
2	**4**	5	**6**

$0 + 4 =$

$2 + 4 =$

$2 + 2 =$ $1 + 3 =$

Exercise 20B

Copy and complete:

1

+	0	1	2	3
0				
1				
2				
3				

2

+	1	2	3	4
3				
4				
5				
6				

3

+	2	3	4	5
2				
3				
4				
5				

4

+	2	3	4	6
1				
2				
3				
4				

5

+	3	4	5	6
0				
1				
2				
3				

6

+	2	4	6	8
1				
2				
3				
4				

Here is a number square for subtraction (−).

−	1	2	③	4	5
10	9	8	7	6	5
9	8	7	6	5	4
⑧	7	6	⑤	4	3
7	6	5	4	3	2

This shows
8 − 3 = 5

Example

Complete the number square:

−	1	2	3	4
7	6	5	4	
6		4		2
5		3		
4	3		1	0

Answer:

−	1	2	3	4
7	6	5	4	**3**
6	5	4	3	2
5	4	3	**2**	1
4	**3**	2	1	0

7 − 4 =

5 − 3 =

4 − 1 =

Exercise 20C

Copy and complete:

1

−	4	5	6
10			
9			
8			
7			

2

−	1	2	3
6			
5			
4			
3			

3

−	3	4	5
9			
8			
7			
6			

4

−	1	2	3	4
9				
8				
7				
6				

5

−	3	4	5	6
10				
9				
8				
7				
6				

6

−	2	3	4
9			
8			
7			
6			
5			

21 Angles 2

Here is a spinner, showing some turns.

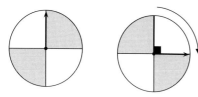

The spinner has turned one quarter of the way round.
This is a **quarter turn**.
It is also called a **right angle**.

You draw a right angle with a small square in the angle like this:

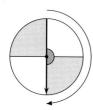

The spinner has turned half the way round.
This is a **half turn**.

You draw half turns like this:

Making a right angle

Take a piece of scrap paper.

Fold in two.

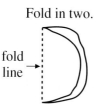

fold line →

Fold again.

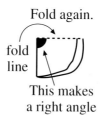

fold line

This makes a right angle

You can use your right angle to check other angles.

Example

Which of these angles are right angles?

A

B

C

The corner of this page is a right angle.

Look to see which are quarter turns.

Answer: A and C

Exercise 21A

1   Which of these are right angles?

2   Which of these are right angles?

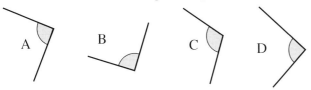

Right angles in shapes

Sometimes you will be asked to list the right angles in a shape.

Example

List the right angles in this shape.

Look at each angle in turn. Is it a right angle?

Answer: A, D, E, F

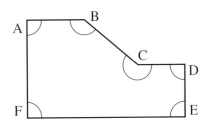

Exercise 21B

List the right angles in these shapes.

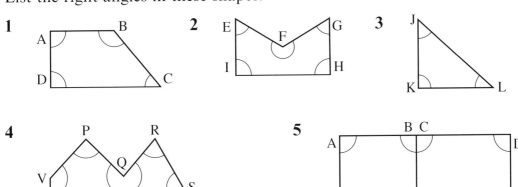

22 Turning shapes

Sometimes you will be asked to turn a shape through an angle.

One way of doing this is to use tracing paper.

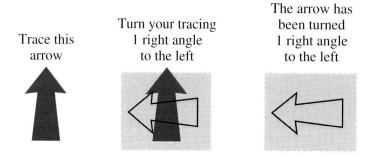

Trace this arrow

Turn your tracing 1 right angle to the left

The arrow has been turned 1 right angle to the left

Example

Turn this shape 2 right angles to the right.

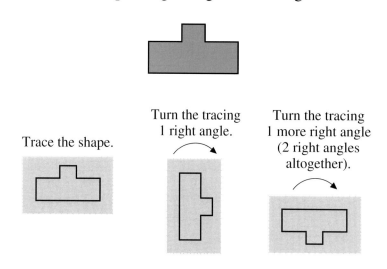

Trace the shape.

Turn the tracing 1 right angle.

Turn the tracing 1 more right angle (2 right angles altogether).

Draw the shape turned 2 right angles.

Answer:

Exercise 22A

Use tracing paper to help you.

Find   **a**   how many right angles has the shape turned.

         b   whether if has turned left or right.

1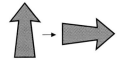

2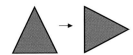

3

4

5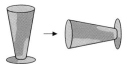

6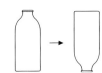

7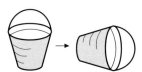

8

Remember

A quarter turn is a right angle.
These are right angles:

The corner of this page is a
right angle.

23 Addition beyond 10

You know how to add numbers up to 10 to find the total.
Sometimes you need to add larger numbers.
Here is a way of adding without a calculator.

Using cubes to add 25 and 13:   Put together this makes:

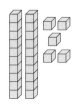   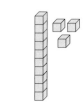   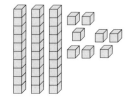

25 is 2 tens and 5 units   13 is 1 ten and 3 units   3 tens and 8 units is 38

This is written:

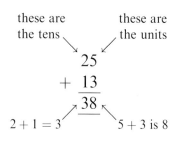

these are
the tens ↘   these are
                   the units ↙

25
+ 13
  38
2 + 1 = 3 ↗   ↖ 5 + 3 is 8

Example

Copy and complete: 21   Answer: 21
                   + 14   + 14
                   ____   35
                                   add the tens ↗   ↖ add the units first
                                   2 + 1 is 3   1 + 4 is 5

Exercise 23A

Copy and complete:

1 **a** 23 **b** 34 **c** 41 **d** 43 **e** 51
        + 15   + 23   + 27   + 35   + 24
        ____   ____   ____   ____   ____

2 **a** 16 **b** 26 **c** 31 **d** 45 **e** 64
        + 12   + 22   + 18   + 21   + 15
        ____   ____   ____   ____   ____

Sometimes when you add the units it comes to more than 10.
Add 17 cubes and 24 cubes.

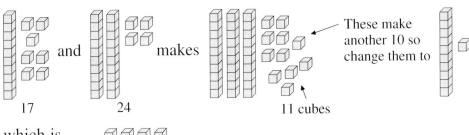

These make
another 10 so
change them to

11 cubes

which is

4 tens and 1 unit = 41

You write this:

$$
\begin{array}{r}
17 \\
+ \;_1 24 \\
\hline
41 \\
\hline
\end{array}
$$

7 + 4 = 11

Add the 'ten'
to the tens

← 1 unit here

1 + 2 + 1

You can also use a
number line to add
the units.

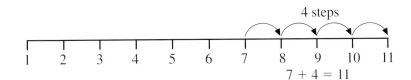

4 steps

7 + 4 = 11

Example

a
$$
\begin{array}{r}
36 \\
+ \;_1 17 \\
\hline
53 \\
\hline
\end{array}
$$
← 6 + 7 = 13
13 is 1 ten and 3 units

b
$$
\begin{array}{r}
28 \\
+ \;_1 47 \\
\hline
75 \\
\hline
\end{array}
$$
← 8 + 7 = 15
15 is 1 ten and 5 units

Exercise 23B

Copy and complete:

1 **a**
$$
\begin{array}{r}
35 \\
+ 27 \\
\hline
\end{array}
$$
b
$$
\begin{array}{r}
48 \\
+ 17 \\
\hline
\end{array}
$$
c
$$
\begin{array}{r}
36 \\
+ 19 \\
\hline
\end{array}
$$
d
$$
\begin{array}{r}
17 \\
+ 26 \\
\hline
\end{array}
$$
e
$$
\begin{array}{r}
23 \\
+ 39 \\
\hline
\end{array}
$$

2 **a**
$$
\begin{array}{r}
14 \\
+ 28 \\
\hline
\end{array}
$$
b
$$
\begin{array}{r}
43 \\
+ 29 \\
\hline
\end{array}
$$
c
$$
\begin{array}{r}
66 \\
+ 25 \\
\hline
\end{array}
$$
d
$$
\begin{array}{r}
57 \\
+ 26 \\
\hline
\end{array}
$$
e
$$
\begin{array}{r}
47 \\
+ 39 \\
\hline
\end{array}
$$

Adding three numbers together

Do these the same way as sums with two numbers.
Remember to start with the units.

Example

a

$$
\begin{array}{r}
27 \\
+\ 15 \\
+\ _1 12 \\
\hline
54 \\
\hline
\end{array}
$$

$2 + 1 + 1 + 1$ ↗ 54 ↘ $7 + 5 + 2 = 14$
14 is 1 ten and 4 units

Using a number line:

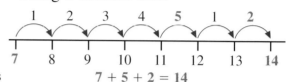

$7 + 5 + 2 = 14$

b

$$
\begin{array}{r}
26 \\
+\ 17 \\
+\ _2 29 \\
\hline
72 \\
\hline
\end{array}
$$

$2 + 1 + 2 + 2$ ↗ 72 ↘ $6 + 7 + 9 = 22$
22 is 2 tens and 2 units

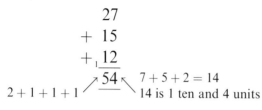

$6 + 7 + 9 = 22$

Exercise 23C

Copy and complete:

1
 a
$$\begin{array}{r} 15 \\ + 11 \\ + 23 \\ \hline \end{array}$$
 b
$$\begin{array}{r} 21 \\ + 16 \\ + 22 \\ \hline \end{array}$$
 c
$$\begin{array}{r} 43 \\ + 24 \\ + 12 \\ \hline \end{array}$$
 d
$$\begin{array}{r} 17 \\ + 21 \\ + 31 \\ \hline \end{array}$$

2
 a
$$\begin{array}{r} 27 \\ + 14 \\ + 18 \\ \hline \end{array}$$
 b
$$\begin{array}{r} 21 \\ + 47 \\ + 36 \\ \hline \end{array}$$
 c
$$\begin{array}{r} 45 \\ + 34 \\ + 24 \\ \hline \end{array}$$
 d
$$\begin{array}{r} 56 \\ + 27 \\ + 18 \\ \hline \end{array}$$

Remember

Always add the units first.
Write units in the units column.
Write tens in the tens column.

tens column ↘   units column ↙

$$
\begin{array}{r}
24 \\
+\ 39 \\
\hline
\end{array}
$$

In reverse

On page 74 you saw how pairs of sums go together, like $6 + 4 = 10$ and $4 + 6 = 10$. This page will show you how other numbers go together.

$$10 + 4 = 14 \qquad 14 - 4 = 10 \qquad 14 - 10 = 4$$

14, 10 and 4 go together for adding and subtracting.

Example $\quad 12 + 13 = 25$

Copy and fill in the missing numbers: Answer:

$$25 - \boxed{} = 12$$
$$25 - \boxed{} = 13$$

$$25 - \boxed{13} = 12$$
$$25 - \boxed{12} = 13$$

The three numbers are used once in each sum.

Exercise 23D

Copy and fill in the missing numbers:

1

a $\quad 14 + 15 = 29$
$29 - \boxed{} = 15$
$29 - \boxed{} = 14$

b $\quad 23 + 7 = 30$
$30 - \boxed{} = 23$
$30 - \boxed{} = 7$

c $\quad 17 + 19 = 36$
$36 - \boxed{} = 17$
$36 - \boxed{} = 19$

d $\quad 52 + 49 = 101$
$101 - \boxed{} = 49$
$101 - \boxed{} = 52$

e $\quad 34 + 27 = 61$
$61 - \boxed{} = 27$
$61 - \boxed{} = 34$

f $\quad 15 + 41 = 56$
$56 - \boxed{} = 15$
$56 - \boxed{} = 41$

Example

Use the numbers 15, 23 and 8 to make three different calculations.

Answer: $\quad 15 + 8 = 23 \qquad 23 - 15 = 8 \qquad 23 - 8 = 15$

Exercise 23E

1 Use the numbers to make three different calculations:

  a 11, 7, 18   **b** 4, 9, 13   **c** 7, 5, 12   **d** 12, 17, 5
  e 15, 11, 4   **f** 21, 4, 25   **g** 12, 14, 26   **h** 9, 8, 17
  i 14, 5, 19   **j** 7, 19, 26   **k** 11, 8, 3   **l** 18, 4, 22

2 Use the numbers to make three different calculations:

  a 15, 24, 39   **b** 91, 14, 77   **c** 15, 42, 27   **d** 19, 43, 62
  e 97, 84, 13   **f** 19, 75, 56   **g** 18, 37, 19   **h** 46, 28, 18
  i 79, 91, 12   **j** 18, 81, 99   **k** 100, 22, 78   **l** 91, 79, 12

24 Rectangles and squares

Rectangles

A rectangle has 4 sides.
All its angles are right angles.
Opposite sides are equal.

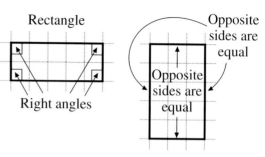

These are rectangles.

This is not a rectangle.

Example

Which sides are equal?

AB and CD are equal.
BC and AD are equal.

Answer: AB = CD   BC = AD

Example

Write the lengths of the sides of this rectangle.

Count the grid squares.

Answer: PQ = 7 cm   QR = 3 cm
          RS = 7 cm   PS = 3 cm

Exercise 24A

1   Which of these shapes are rectangles?

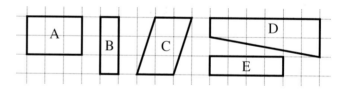

2   Which sides are equal?

a

WX = YZ
XY = ?

b, c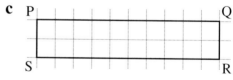

d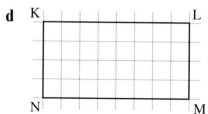

3 Write the lengths of the sides of these rectangles in grid squares.

a

b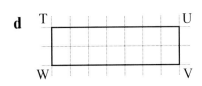

c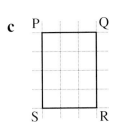

d

e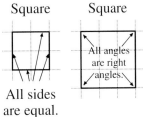

Squares

A square is a special rectangle.
All its angles are right angles.
All 4 sides are equal.

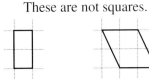

Square   Square   These are not squares.

All sides are equal.   All angles are right angles.   The 4 sides are not equal.   The angles are not right angles.

Example

a Write the lengths of the sides of these shapes.
b Check that all angles are right angles.
c Which of these shapes are squares?

1   **2**

Count the grid squares.
Answer:

1 a Count the squares
   $AB = 2$, $BC = 2$
   $CD = 2$, $AD = 2$
b All angles are right angles.
c This is a square.

2 a $WX = 1$, $XY = 1$
   $YZ = 1$, $WZ = 1$
b All angles are right angles.
c This is a square.

Exercise 24B

1   Which of these shapes
    are squares?

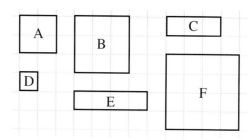

2   These shapes are drawn on centimetre squared paper.
    a   Write down the lengths of the sides of each shape in cm.
    b   Check all angles are right angles.
    c   Which of these shapes are squares?

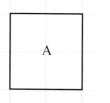
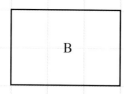

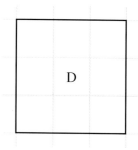

3   Which of these are rectangles? Which of these are squares?

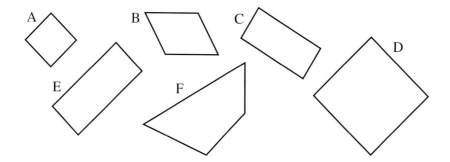

Remember

Rectangles have opposite sides equal.

Rectangles have 4 right angles.

A square is a rectangle with 4 equal sides.

Rectangle   Square

25 Subtraction

You can add numbers larger than 10. This page shows
you how to do subtractions with larger numbers.

Using cubes

24 − 7
24 take away 7

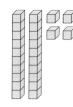

Swap a ten
for 10 units.

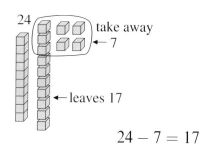

24

take away
← 7

← leaves 17

24 − 7 = 17

Example

Work out 35 − 19

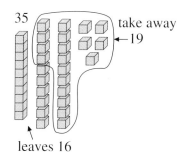

35

take away
← 19

leaves 16

Answer: 35 − 19 = 16

Exercise 25A

1   Use cubes for these. Work out:

    a   23 − 5   **b**   25 − 8   **c**   32 − 6   **d**   42 − 17   **e**   32 − 15
    f   24 − 7   **g**   38 − 12   **h**   21 − 8   **i**   34 − 15   **j**   47 − 29

2   Check your answers with a calculator.

Page 77 shows you how to use a
calculator for subtraction.

Subtraction in steps

24 − 7   take away 7 in *sensible steps*

              take 4 to go to nearest whole ten

24 − 4 = 20
     ↓   7 − 4 = 3   so take away 3 more
    20 − 3 = 17

so   24 − 7 = 17

Example

Work out $27 - 13$

$$27 - 7 = 20 \qquad 13 - 7 = 6, \text{ so take away 6 more}$$
$$\downarrow \qquad \nearrow$$
$$20 - 6 = 14$$

Answer: $27 - 13 = 14$

Exercise 25B

Work out:

1 **a** $25 - 9$ **b** $28 - 11$ **c** $34 - 15$ **d** $22 - 14$
    e $42 - 15$ **f** $37 - 18$ **g** $21 - 9$ **h** $37 - 18$

2   Check your answers with a calculator.

Using addition

To find $24 - 7$ using addition,
start with 7 and count on to 24.
Use cubes to help.

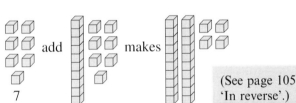

7   add   makes

(See page 105
'In reverse'.)

$$7 + \boxed{17} = 24 \quad \text{so} \quad 24 - 7 = 17$$

Example

Work out $32 - 18$

Use addition $18 + \square = 32$

Count on $18 + 14 = 32$

Answer: $32 - 18 = 14$

Exercise 25C

1 **a** $54 - 35$ **b** $27 - 11$ **c** $34 - 25$ **d** $45 - 29$
    e $65 - 39$ **f** $73 - 54$ **g** $36 - 27$ **h** $55 - 39$

2   Check your answers with a calculator.

Remember

$10 + 4 = 14$ $\qquad$ $14 - 4 = 10$ $\qquad$ $14 - 10 = 4$ $\qquad$ all go together.

Example

Find the missing number $\boxed{} - 72 = 14$

$\boxed{} - 72 = 14$ $\qquad$ $\boxed{} - 14 = 72$ $\qquad$ $72 + 14 = \boxed{}$ $\qquad$ all go together.

Work out $\quad 72 + 14 = \boxed{86}$

Answer: $\boxed{86} - 72 = 14$

Example

Find the missing number:

$\qquad \boxed{} - 12 = 14$

The sums that go together are

$\qquad \boxed{} - 12 = 14$ $\qquad$ $\boxed{} - 14 = 12$ $\qquad$ $12 + 14 = \boxed{}$ $\leftarrow$ Work this out

$\qquad 12 + 14 = \boxed{26}$

Answer: $\boxed{26} - 12 = 14$

Exercise 25D

Copy and fill in the missing numbers.

1   **a** $\boxed{} - 12 = 20$ **b** $31 - \boxed{} = 14$ **c** $\boxed{} - 25 = 43$

    d $74 - \boxed{} = 36$ **e** $\boxed{} - 27 = 15$ **f** $36 - \boxed{} = 15$

    g $\boxed{} - 23 = 24$ **h** $84 - \boxed{} = 53$ **i** $\boxed{} - 38 = 54$

    j $63 - \boxed{} = 14$ **k** $72 - \boxed{} = 13$ **l** $\boxed{} - 11 = 52$

2   Choose the method you prefer to work out:

    a $29 - 15$ **b** $30 - 23$ **c** $36 \quad 17$ **d** $98 - 49$

    e $77 - 55$ **f** $61 - 34$ **g** $124 - 73$ **h** $143 - 98$

    i $171 - 19$ **j** $75 - 38$ **k** $134 - 76$ **l** $193 - 154$

3   Check your answers with a calculator.

26 Shopping problems

When you buy several items at once you need to be able
to add the prices to find the total cost.

Find the total cost.
Use money or cubes to help.

Using money:

Using cubes:

Example

Work out the total cost of

Use cubes or
money.

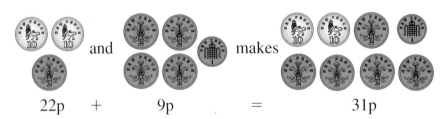

Exercise 26A

Work out the total cost of:

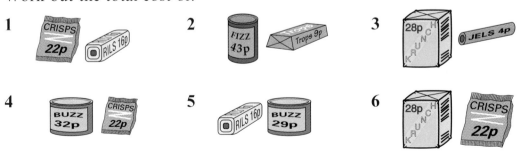

Example

Work out the total cost of

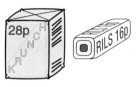 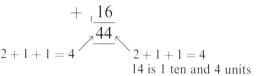

Use cubes, money or an addition sum.

Answer: 44p

$$\begin{array}{r} 28 \\ + \ _1 16 \\ \hline 44 \end{array}$$

2 + 1 + 1 = 4   2 + 1 + 1 = 4
14 is 1 ten and 4 units

Exercise 26B

Work out the total cost.

1

2

3

4

5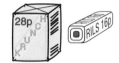

6

Finding the total for three items

Add the three prices in an addition sum.

Example

Work out the total cost of:

Answer: 69p

$$\begin{array}{r} 22 \\ + 43 \\ + \ \ 4 \\ \hline 69 \end{array}$$

2 + 4   2 + 3 + 4 = 9

Exercise 26C

1 Work out the total cost of:

a

b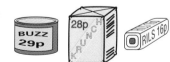

c

d

Working out the change

If you pay for your shopping with £1, you need to work out how much change you'll get.

Remember
£1 = 100p.

Example

i   Work out the total cost of 28p, 43p and 16p.
ii   Work out the change you will get from £1.

i
```
   28
 + 43
 + 16    8 + 3 + 6 = 17
 ----
   87
```

Answer: 87p

ii   Use coins to count on from 87p to £1.

Count to the nearest 10p.

87p + makes 90p

and 90p + makes £1

Count on in ten pences.

so 87p + is £1.

Answer: 13p   This is the change: 13p

Exercise 26D

Find   i   the total cost and   ii   the change from £1.

1   a   22p, 29p, 4p   b   29p, 28p, 9p   c   22p, 16p, 9p
    d   43p, 16p, 4p   e   9p, 16p, 4p   f   29p, 22p, 16p
    g   43p, 22p, 9p   h   28p, 16p, 4p   i   28p, 9p, 16p
    j   43p, 16p, 22p

2   a   25p, 42p, 15p   b   15p, 19p, 4p   c   17p, 24p, 5p
    d   12p, 5p, 34p   e   23p, 14p, 2p   f   42p, 11p, 7p
    g   15p, 17p, 6p   h   19p, 27p, 4p   i   9p, 52p, 8p
    j   18p, 24p, 15p

3   Use a calculator to check your answers. Remember £1 is 100p.

Remember

To find the total cost, you add up the prices.

27 Vertices and sides

You need to be able to count the vertices and sides in a shape.
Vertices are corners.

This shape has 6 sides.
This shape has 6 vertices.

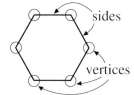

Example

How many sides?
How many vertices?

Count them:

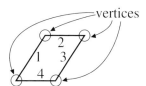

Answer: 4 sides, 4 vertices

Exercise 27A

How many sides? How many vertices?

1   2   3

4    5   6

7   8   9

Triangles

This is a triangle.
It has 3 sides.
It has 3 vertices.

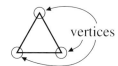

These are all triangles.

Exercise 27B

Which of these shapes are triangles?

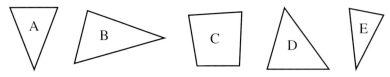

Drawing shapes

Sometimes you will be asked to draw a shape with a given number of sides and vertices.

Example

Draw a shape with 4 sides and 4 vertices.

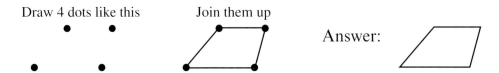

Draw 4 dots like this   Join them up   Answer:

Exercise 27C

1   Draw a shape with 5 sides and 5 vertices.
Copy these 5 dots.
Join them up.

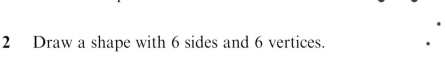

2   Draw a shape with 6 sides and 6 vertices.

3   Draw a shape with 9 sides and 9 vertices.

4   Draw a shape with 10 sides and 10 vertices.

Circles and curves

This circle has 1 curved side and no vertices.

This shape has 3 curved sides and 3 vertices.

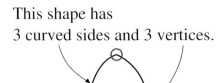

Example

How many curved sides? How many vertices?

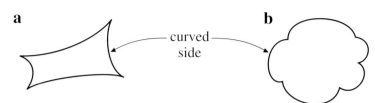

Answer: 4 curved sides, 4 vertices.   Answer: 5 curved sides, 5 vertices

Exercise 27D

How many curved sides? How many vertices?

1   **2**   **3**

4   **5**    **6**

7 Which shapes are triangles?

8 Which shapes are rectangles?

9 Which shapes are squares?

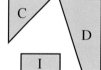

10 A rectangle
How many sides?
How many vertices?

11 A square
How many sides?
How many vertices?

Remember

Vertex means corner. Vertices means corners.

Circle   Triangle   Square   Rectangle

28 How much more?

In a shop two similar items often have different prices.
You can use subtraction (see p. 109) to find the price difference.

    Whoosh costs more than Swish.

Example

a   Which costs more?
b   How much more?

a   Answer: 74 is bigger than 58 so stock mix costs more.
b   Subtract to find how much more:

$$74p - 58p = 16p$$

Answer: 16p more

Exercise 28A

a   Which costs more?   **b**   How much more?

1 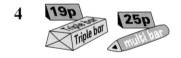 *(FIZZ 28p / BUZZ 42p)*

2 CRACKS 36p / scrunch 67p

3 45p / 32p

4 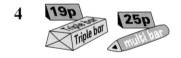 Triple bar 19p / multi bar 25p

5 giant gels 34p / mint gels 50p

6 1st 26p / 2nd 20p

7 MAGS 95p / Rags 87p

8 CHOC DROPS 78p / fruit drops 63p

9 Super Pen 94p / maxi pen 65p

10 23p / 15p

11 cheesies 32p / Crackers 27p

12 PEAS 26p / Carrots 38p

13 Beans 34p / Pasta 45p

14 63p / 49p

15 GLUE PEN 72p / GLUE STICK 89p

16 Devon Ice 52p / cream ice 70p

17 Farmhouse 78p / Whole grain 94p

18 Carrots 67p / Potatoes 48p

Problems

Sometimes problems are written in words.
If a problem asks 'How much more?' you have to
subtract to find the difference.

Example

Susan gets £5 pocket money.
Martin earns £20 in a shop.

a Who gets more?   **b** How much more?

a 20 is bigger than 5.
Answer: Martin gets more.

b Subtract to find how much more.

$$20 - 5 = 15$$

Answer: £15 more

Exercise 28B

1 John gets £8 pocket money. His brother earns £14.
   Who gets more? How much more?

2 Anita gets £20 for her birthday. Neema gets £15.
   Who gets more? How much more?

3 William has 24 football cards, Jenny has 18.
   Who has more? How many more?

4 Mark has 35 model cars.
   Jerry has 52 model cars.
   Who has more? How many more?

5 Ruth has 30 coloured pens.
   Nick has 45 coloured pens.
   Who has more? How many more?

At the supermarket

This exercise will give you more practice in using addition to find the total cost.

Example

Work out the total cost of Pasta, Beans and Rils.
Write the prices in a list.

$$\begin{array}{ll} \text{Pasta} & 45\text{p} \\ \text{Beans} & 34\text{p} \\ \text{Rils} & \underline{{}_1 16\text{p}} \\ & 95\text{p} \end{array}$$

Add them up

$4 + 3 + 1 + 1 = 9$ $5 + 4 + 6 = 15$

Answer: 95p

Exercise 28C

Work out the total cost of:

1 Buzz, Gingerbread man and Jels   2 Farmhouse and Triple bar

3 Devon Ice, Beans and Slicks   4 Peas, Triple bar and Rils

5 Stock cubes, Jels and Gums   6 Potatoes, Rils and Slicks

7 Triple bar, Jels, Gums and Rils   8 Buzz, Crisps and Gingerbread man

9 Farmhouse, Crisps and Jels   10 Beans, Peas and Gums

11 Stock cubes, Crisps, Peas   12 Rils, Gums and Crisps

13 Pasta and Devon ice   14 Devon Ice, Crisps and Slicks

15 Peas, Crisps and Buzz   16 3 packets of crisps

Remember

Which costs more? Pick the **largest** number.
B has the largest number. B costs more.

A

B

29 Programming journeys

Here is a robot used in a factory
to transport equipment.

You can program the robot to
make journeys.

The robot understands these instructions:

forward ____ squares
turn right
turn left   You have to tell it how many squares.
stop

Writing programs

Here is a journey:

You would write the program like this:

forward 3 squares
turn right
forward 4 squares
stop

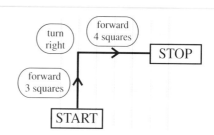

Sometimes you are given a map of the journey the robot has to make. You
need to write the robot's program.

Example

Write the robot's program.   Answer: forward 3 squares
                                                 turn left
                                                 forward 9 squares
                                                 stop

Exercise 29A

Write the programs for these journeys.

1
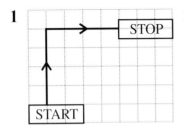

2
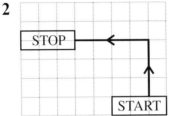

3
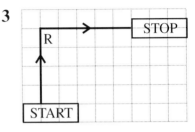

4
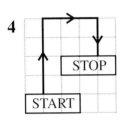

5
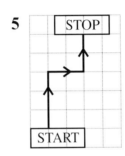

6
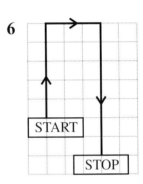

Drawing journeys

Sometimes you will be given instructions and asked to draw the robot's journey.

Example

Draw this journey:

       start

       forward 3 squares

       turn left

       forward 3 squares

       stop

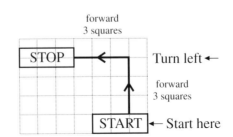

Exercise 29B

Draw these journeys on squared paper.

1   start
forward 4 squares
turn left
forward 3 squares
stop

2   start
forward 2 squares
turn left
forward 3 squares
stop

3   start
forward 4 squares
turn right
forward 2 squares
stop

4   start
forward 5 squares
turn right
forward 3 squares
turn left
forward 1 square
stop

5   start
forward 4 squares
turn left
forward 4 squares
turn right
forward 4 squares
stop

6   start
forward 6 squares
turn right
forward 3 squares
turn right
forward 2 squares
stop

7   start
forward 3 squares
turn left
forward 4 squares
turn left
forward 5 squares
stop

8   start
forward 2 squares
turn right
forward 3 squares
turn right
forward 4 squares
stop

9   start
forward 3 squares
turn left
forward 2 squares
turn left
forward 3 squares
stop

Remember

Use your hands to tell right and left.

30 Solids

Solid shapes have vertices just like flat shapes.
The flat sides are called **faces**.
Where two faces meet is an **edge**.

This solid has

12 vertices
8 faces
18 edges.

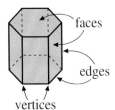

Example

How many vertices, faces and edges has this cube?

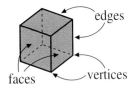

Answer: 8 vertices
6 faces
12 edges

Note   The dotted lines show the edges at the back of the solid.

Exercise 30A

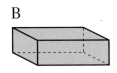

Copy and complete this table for these solids.

Solid	Vertices	Faces	Edges
A			
B			
C			

Boxes from cubes

Example

Use 12 cubes. Make them into a box.

Answer: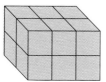

Example

Make this box.
How many cubes are needed to make it? Count the cubes.

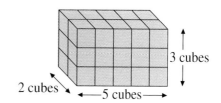

Answer: 30 cubes

Remember

A dice is a cube.

A sugar lump is a cube.

You use cubes for counting.

Exercise 30B

Make these boxes. How many cubes in each?

1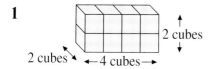

2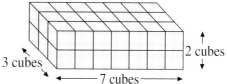

3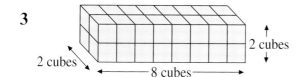

4

5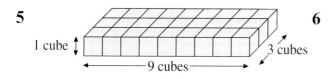

6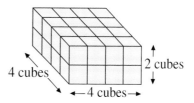

7   Use 18 cubes to make a box.
8   Use 20 cubes to make a box.
9   Use 24 cubes to make a box.
10   Use 16 cubes to make a box.

31 Matching diagrams

You already know how to read and present information in tables. Matching diagrams are another way of presenting information.

Here is a matching diagram showing children's ages.

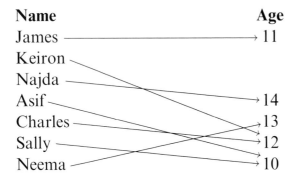

To read the information, follow the arrows.
James is 11.

Asif and Sally are 10.

Example

Copy and complete this matching diagram.

Join the words to the pictures with arrows.

Answer:

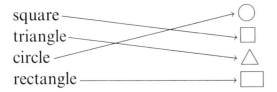

Exercise 31A

Copy and complete these matching diagrams.

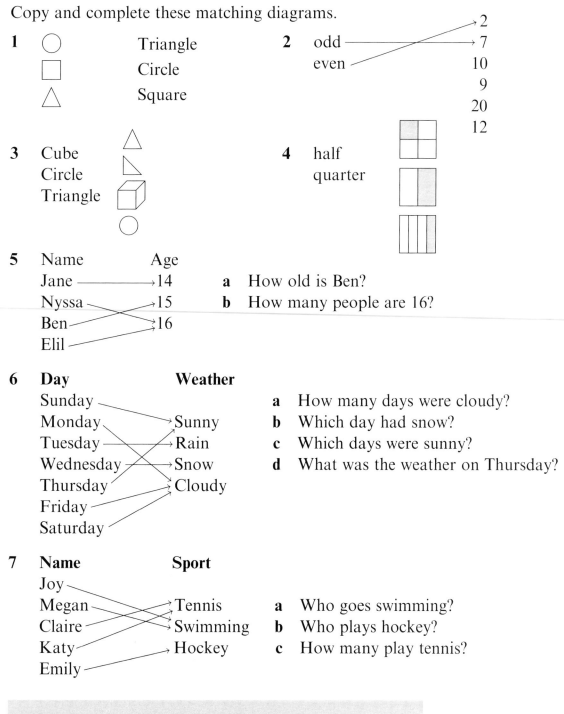

1   ○   Triangle
       □   Circle
       △   Square

2   odd ⟶ 2
             ⟶ 7
       even   10
                   9
                   20
                   12

3   Cube
       Circle
       Triangle

4   half
       quarter

5   Name   Age
       Jane ⟶ 14   **a**   How old is Ben?
       Nyssa ⟶ 15   **b**   How many people are 16?
       Ben ⟶ 16
       Elil

6   **Day**   **Weather**
       Sunday   **a**   How many days were cloudy?
       Monday ⟶ Sunny   **b**   Which day had snow?
       Tuesday ⟶ Rain   **c**   Which days were sunny?
       Wednesday ⟶ Snow   **d**   What was the weather on Thursday?
       Thursday ⟶ Cloudy
       Friday
       Saturday

7   **Name**   **Sport**
       Joy
       Megan ⟶ Tennis   **a**   Who goes swimming?
       Claire ⟶ Swimming   **b**   Who plays hockey?
       Katy ⟶ Hockey   **c**   How many play tennis?
       Emily

Remember

Follow the arrows to find the answer.

32 Lots and lots

If you have several sets of objects, counting them can
take a long time.
Multiplication is a quicker way of finding how many
there are.

How many cakes?

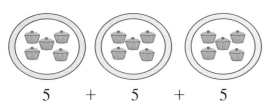 is the same as 3 lots of 5.

    5   +   5   +   5

In maths you write this as 3×5.
This is called multiplication.

For 3×5 you say 3 times 5 or 3 multiply 5.

3×5 is a multiplication.

multiplication sign

Example

How many tickets?

Write this as a multiplication.

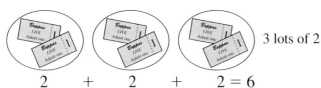 3 lots of 2

    2   +   2   +   2 = 6

multiplication: 3 times $2 = 3 \times 2 = 6$ Answer: 6 tickets

Exercise 32A

1 **a** How many eggs?
      Write the multiplication.

     b How many tennis balls?
        Write the multiplication.

    c How many videos?
       Write the multiplication.

     d How many golf clubs?
        Write the multiplication.

Example

Humbugs cost 4p each. How much are 3 humbugs?

4p + 4p + 4p is 3 × 4p   3 × 4p = 12p

Answer: 12p

Exercise 32B

1 **a**   Labels cost 5p each. How much are 4 labels?
   b   Pencils cost 6p each. How much are 3 pencils?
   c   Biscuits cost 4p each. How much are 6 biscuits?
   d   Gums cost 5p each. How much are 5 gums?

When objects are arranged in rows you can use multiplication to work out how many there are.

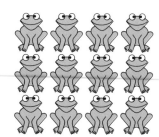

4 frogs in each of 3 lines

4 + 4 + 4 = 12

is the same as

3 × 4 = 12

Exercise 32C

1   How many biros?

2   How many eggs?

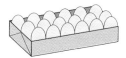

3   How many coins?

4   How many cartons?

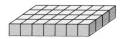

5   How many stock cubes?

6   How many glue sticks?

7   How many glasses?

8   How many cans?

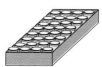

You can use multiplication to work out how many squares there are in a grid.

Use this muiplication grid to help you:

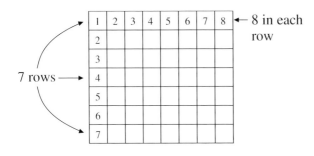

Example

How many small squares are in this grid?

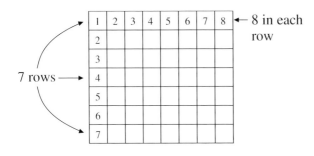

$8 \times 7 = 56$

8 squares in each row for 7 rows.

Answer: $8 \times 7 = 56$

Exercise 32D

How many small squares are in each grid? Write down the multiplication.

1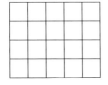

2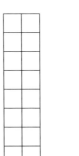

3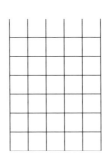

4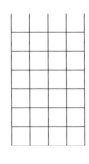

5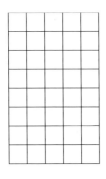

6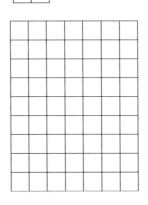

7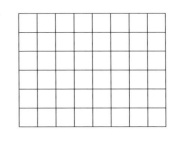

Drawing arrangements

If you have some items to pack in a box there may be
several ways you can arrange them.

Example

On squared paper draw an arrangement to show 24.
There are several ways of showing 24 squares.

Answer:

This is one
arrangement:

Here is
another:

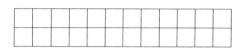

$6 \times 4 = 24$

$2 \times 12 = 24$

Exercise 32E

On squared paper draw arrangements for these:

1 **a** 16   **b** 18   **c** 20   **d** 50   **e** 30
   f 48   **g** 60   **h** 28   **i** 36

2 Draw a different arrangement for each of the numbers in question **1**.

3 Draw arrangements of squares for:
   a 7×9 **b** 6×7 **c** 5×3 **d** 4×8 **e** 8×3 **f** 2×4
   g 5×8 **h** 3×9 **i** 4×7 **j** 5×5 **k** 6×6 **l** 7×7
   m 2×6 **n** 7×3 **o** 9×9 **p** 8×5 **q** 4×4 **r** 3×3

4 How many squares are there in each part of question **3**?
   Use multiplication.

Remember

These give the
same answer:

$7 + 7 + 7$ 3 lots of 7 3×7 3 multiply 7   3 times 7

33 Sharing

Suppose you have 20p, and sweets are 3p each.
You need to be able to work out how many sweets you
can buy.

Biscuits cost 4p each.
You have 20p. How many biscuits can you buy?

Method 1
Share the money into groups.

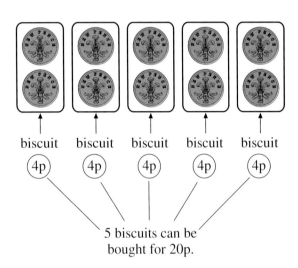

biscuit   biscuit   biscuit   biscuit   biscuit
(4p)   (4p)   (4p)   (4p)   (4p)

5 biscuits can be
bought for 20p.

20p split into groups of 4p is 5 groups
20p   divided by   4p = 5
20p   ÷   4p = 5
                    This is divide or share.

Method 2
Subtraction.
Take away
4p each
time.

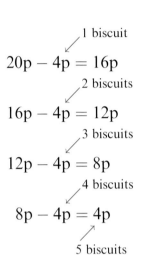

$$20p - 4p = 16p$$
$$16p - 4p = 12p$$
$$12p - 4p = 8p$$
$$8p - 4p = 4p$$

1 biscuit
2 biscuits
3 biscuits
4 biscuits
5 biscuits

Example

How many 5p gums can I buy with 20p?

Method 1
20p is

Answer: $20p \div 5p = 4$

Method 2
Step 1 $20p - 5p = 15p$
Step 2 $15p - 5p = 10p$
Step 3 $10p - 5p = 5p$
Step 4 $5p - 5p = 0$

So $20p \div 5p = 4$

Exercise 33A

Use the method you prefer.

1   How many 5p lollies can I buy with 15p?

2   How many 3p sweets can I buy with 12p?

3   How many 4p stickers can I buy with 40p?

4   How many 5p pencils can I buy with 25p?

5   How many 2p mints can I buy with 10p?

Here is a chocolate bar.

How can you share this bar fairly
between 3 people?

12 squares

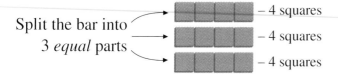

Split the bar into
   3 *equal* parts

– 4 squares
– 4 squares
– 4 squares

We say   12 shared equally between 3 is 4 each
          12   divided by   3 is 4
          12   ÷   3 = 4

Example

Share £20 equally between 5 people. How much for each person?

shared between 5 people

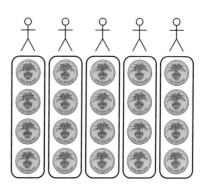

£20

Each person gets £4

Answer: £20 ÷ 5 = £4

Exercise 33B

1   Here is a chocolate bar with 15 pieces.
    Share 15 equally between 3 people.
    How much for each person?

2   Share £24 equally between 4 people. How much for each person?

3   Share £25 equally between 5 people. How much for each person?

4   Share £30 equally between 3 people. How much for each person?

5   Share 14 sweets equally between 2 people. How many for each person?

6   Share 25 counters equally between 5 people. How many for each person?

7   Share 18 biscuits between 6 people. How much for each person?

8   Share £24 between 6 people. How much for each person?

Using a calculator

To share 18 sweets equally between 3 people

press $\boxed{1}\boxed{8}\boxed{\div}\boxed{3}\boxed{=}$ giving $\boxed{6.}$

Write $18 \div 3 = 6$ sweets

Example

Share £72 equally between 9 people.
How many for each person?

press $\boxed{7}\boxed{2}\boxed{\div}\boxed{9}\boxed{=}$ giving $\boxed{8.}$

Answer: $£72 \div 9 = £8$

Exercise 33C

Use a calculator.

1   Share £60 equally between 10 people.
    How much for each person?

2   Share £36 equally between 9 people.
    How much for each person?

3 Share £24 equally between 3 people.
How much for each person?

4 Share £45 equally between 9 people.
How much for each person?

5 Share £80 equally between 8 people.
How much for each person?

You can use dividing to work out how many boxes you need for packing.

Example

Eggs are packed 6 in a box.
How many boxes are needed for 30 eggs?

30 eggs, put 6 in a box

Check using a calculator.

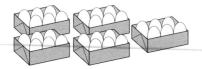

5 boxes

3 0 $\div$ 6 $=$ ⟮ 5. ⟯

Answer: $30 \div 6 = 5$

Exercise 33D

1 I want to make omelettes with 12 eggs.
Each omelette uses 2 eggs.
How many omelettes can I make?

2 Light bulbs are being packed 3 in a box.
How many boxes are needed for 21 bulbs?

3 Share £50 equally between 5 people.
How many for each person?

4 A class of 24 are put in teams of 4.
How many teams are there?

5 42 eggs are packed in boxes of 6.
How many boxes are needed?

Remember
Share
Divide ────▶ These all mean the same.
÷

Gold Contents

1 Hundreds, tens and units

You have already seen how to write numbers up to 100, for example, 42 is forty two.

You write numbers bigger than 100 like this:

127 is one hundred and twenty seven   630 is six hundred and thirty
293 is two hundred and ninety three   807 is eight hundred and seven

You always write the word **and** after the word hundred.

Exercise 1A

Write these numbers in words.

a   436   b   851   c   714

Example

Write the number five hundred and forty nine in figures.
Answer: 549

Exercise 1B

Write these numbers in figures.

a   six hundred and forty two   b   nine hundred and twenty three
c   eight hundred and sixteen   d   three hundred and four

Number values

374 and 437 both use the same numbers: 3, 4 and 7.
The value of the number 4 is not the same.

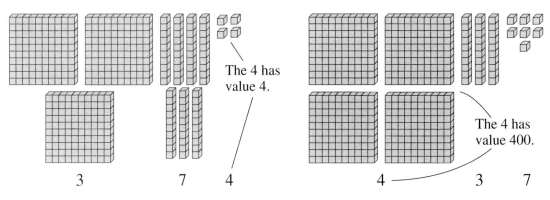

The 4 has value 4.

The 4 has value 400.

400 is larger than 4.

Example

Write down the value of the number 3 in 531 in figures and words.

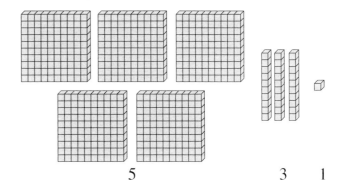

Picture the cubes:

3 has value 30

Answer: 30, thirty

5   3   1

Exercise 1C

1 Write down the value of the number 5 in figures and words.
   a 527   **b** 725   **c** 351   **d** 534   **e** 651

2 Write down the value of the number 7 in figures and words.
   a 273   **b** 738   **c** 417   **d** 276   **e** 667

3 Write down the value of the number 9 in figures and words.
   a 309   **b** 976   **c** 396   **d** 944   **e** 792

Example

Write down the value of the 5 in 352 and 523.
Which is larger?

Answer: 352: 5 has value 50.
           523: 5 has value 500. 500 is larger than 50.

Exercise 1D

Write down the value of the bold numbers. Which is larger?
1 2**5**7, **5**72   2 6**4**2, 2**6**4   3 5**5**2, 2**5**5
4 **9**87, 8**9**7   5 3**7**8, 87**3**

Ordering

You can write numbers in order. Ordering numbers
makes it easy to compare them.

Example

Write in order, smallest first: 769   388   199   642

Look at the numbers of 100s.   769   388   199   642

                                  700   300   100   600

Order the hundreds, smallest first.

           100   300   600   700
Answer: 199   388   642   769

Example

Write in order, smallest first: 652   539   496   673

Look at the numbers of 100s.   652   539   496   673

                                 600   500   400   600

Order the 100s, smallest first: 400,   500,   600,   600

                                  These two numbers are the same so
                                  you must look at the next number.

                                       652,   673

                                       50   70

50 is smaller than 70 so 652 is smaller than 673.

               400   500   650   670
The final order is: 496   539   652   673

Exercise 1E

Write in order, smallest first:
1   900, 100, 750, 500, 950
2   591, 439, 117, 950, 337
3   349, 271, 564, 891, 589
4   711, 299, 438, 99, 774

                      99 has no hundreds

If the 100s and the 10s are the same, you need to look at
the units.

Example

Write in order, largest first: 531   977   931   978   289

Look at the 100s first and put them in order
largest first 900 before 500 before 200

then 10s, 70 before 30

Answer: 9_7_8,   9_7_7,   9_3_1,   531,   289

then units, 8 before 7

Exercise 1F

Write in order, largest first:
1   249, 55, 667, 934, 228
2   602, 287, 634, 909, 306, 659
3   911, 322, 657, 29, 652, 718
4   321, 771, 707, 229, 23, 853

Making numbers

You can make every number using the digits
    0, 1, 2, 3, 4, 5, 6, 7, 8, 9.

Digit is another
word for number.

For example, you use the digits 7, 8 and 9 to make the number 897.

Example

Make the largest number with the digits [4] [7] [6].
Write the number in figures and words.

For the *largest* number:

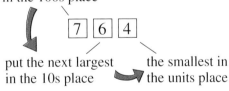

put the largest digit
in the 100s place

[7] [6] [4]

put the next largest
in the 10s place

the smallest in
the units place

Answer: 764, seven hundred and sixty four

Exercise 1G

Make the largest number using these digits.
Write the number in figures and words.

a   [5] [7] [2]   b   [2] [1] [8]   c   [7] [9] [8]
d   [3] [2] [6]   e   [8] [3] [5]   f   [6] [9] [9]

Example

Make the smallest number with $\boxed{4}\ \boxed{7}\ \boxed{6}$

Write the number in figures and words.

For the *smallest* number: put the smallest number
in the 100s place

$\boxed{4}\ \boxed{6}\ \boxed{7}$

the next smallest in   the largest in
the 10s place   the units place

Answer: 467, four hundred and sixty seven

Exercise 1H

Make the smallest number using these digits.
Write each number in figures and words.

a $\boxed{6}\ \boxed{1}\ \boxed{7}$ b $\boxed{2}\ \boxed{1}\ \boxed{2}$ c $\boxed{8}\ \boxed{7}\ \boxed{2}$

d $\boxed{9}\ \boxed{2}\ \boxed{3}$ e $\boxed{5}\ \boxed{7}\ \boxed{3}$ f $\boxed{8}\ \boxed{4}\ \boxed{9}$

Writing in hundreds, tens and units

769 is seven hundred and sixty nine

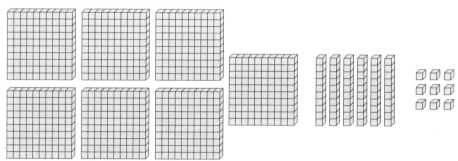

7 Hundreds   6 Tens   9 Units

We can write this in a table.

Hundreds	Tens	Units
7	6	9

When you add numbers you add the units first then the
tens and then the hundreds. Writing them in the correct
columns will help you get this right.

Example

Write the number 621 in Hundreds, Tens and Units columns.

Answer:

Hundreds	Tens	Units
6	2	1

Exercise 1I

Write these numbers in Hundreds, Tens and Units columns.

a 691   **b** 342   **c** 765   **d** 429   **e** 575
f 72   **g** 11   **h** 99   **i** 3

<u>H</u>undreds, <u>T</u>ens and <u>U</u>nits can be written **H**, **T**, **U** for short.

Example

Write these numbers in H, T, U columns.

724,   139,   7,   12,   518

Answer:

H	T	U
7	2	4
1	3	9
		7
	1	2
5	1	8

Exercise 1J

Write these numbers in H, T, U columns.

a 739, 5, 34, 18, 513   **b** 843, 23, 88, 1, 530
c 333, 33, 30, 303, 13   **d** 551, 51, 15, 5, 515
e 999, 97, 79, 17, 9, 699   **f** 539, 843, 65, 691, 2

> **Remember** When you fill in the table always write
> the units first then
> the tens then
> the hundreds.

2 Addition

You can add numbers up to 20, using cubes or a number line.

If you learn the pairs of numbers that add to 20 it will save you a lot of time when you add larger numbers.

Reminder:
Using cubes

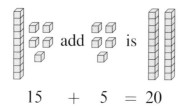

$$15 \quad + \quad 5 \quad = 20$$

Example

Work out $17 + 3$

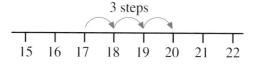

3 steps

15 16 17 18 19 20 21 22

Answer: $17 + 3 = 20$

Exercise 2A

Work out:

1	$12 + 8$	**2**	$9 + 11$	**3**	$14 + 6$	**4**	$10 + 10$	**5**	$4 + 16$
6	$2 + 18$	**7**	$19 + 1$	**8**	$7 + 13$	**9**	$5 + 15$	**10**	$13 + 7$

When you add larger numbers, write them in H, T, U columns first.

Example

Complete
```
  H T U
    2 4
+   1 2
  ─────
```

Answer:
```
  H T U
    2 4
+   1 2
  ─────
    3 6
```
$2 + 1 = 3$ $4 + 2 = 6$

First add the units, then the tens.

Exercise 2B

Copy and complete:

1
```
H T U
  1 1
+ 1 7
─────
```
2
```
H T U
  2 7
+ 3 1
─────
```
3
```
H T U
  7 1
+ 1 4
─────
```
4
```
H T U
  2 4
+ 3 3
─────
```
5
```
H T U
  3 3
+ 1 6
─────
```

You can add even larger numbers in the same way. First write the numbers in H, T, U columns.

Example

Complete
```
H T U
1 3 2
+ 4 2 5
─────
```

Answer:
```
H T U
1 3 2
+ 4 2 5
─────
5 5 7
```

First add the units: $2 + 5 = 7$
then the tens: $3 + 2 = 5$
then the hundreds: $1 + 4 = 5$

Exercise 2C

Copy and complete:

1
```
H T U
2 4 5
+ 1 3 3
─────
```

2
```
H T U
1 4 7
+ 5 1 2
─────
```

3
```
H T U
1 7 2
+ 6 1 6
─────
```

4
```
H T U
7 2 4
+ 1 5 3
─────
```

5
```
H T U
6 4 4
+ 1 2 2
─────
```

6
```
H T U
7 3 4
+ 1 2 1
─────
```

7
```
H T U
6 5 5
+ 2 1 3
─────
```

8
```
H T U
4 1 9
+ 4 2 0
─────
```

9
```
H T U
7 7 3
+ 1 1 5
─────
```

10
```
H T U
6 0 6
+ 2 8 2
─────
```

Sometimes you will be asked to fill in the missing number(s) in a sum.

Example

Complete
```
H T U
3 1 2
+ 2 2 1
─────
5 □ 3
```

Answer:
```
H T U
3 1 2
+ 2 2 1
─────
5 3 3
```

Work out the addition to fill in the missing number.

For the 10s: $1 + 2 = 3$

Exercise 2D

Copy and complete:

1
```
H T U
4 3 2
+ 1 4 5
─────
5 □ 7
```

2
```
H T U
5 2 4
+ 2 3 4
─────
7 5 □
```

3
```
H T U
2 4 1
+ 3 2 6
─────
□ 6 7
```

4
```
H T U
6 7 5
+ 2 1 3
─────
8 □ 8
```

Carrying numbers

If the numbers in the units column add to more than 10, you have to 'carry' the 10 over to the 10s column. This example shows you what happens.

Using cubes: $236 + 147$

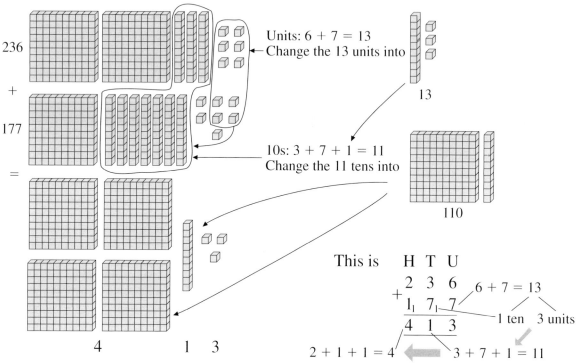

236

+

177

=

Units: $6 + 7 = 13$
Change the 13 units into

13

10s: $3 + 7 + 1 = 11$
Change the 11 tens into

110

4   1   3

This is

H	T	U
2	3	6
1	7	7
4	1	3

$6 + 7 = 13$

1 ten   3 units

$2 + 1 + 1 = 4$ $3 + 7 + 1 = 11$

Example

Complete

H	T	U
5	2	3
+1	4	9

Answer:

H	T	U
5	2	3
+1	4	9
6	7	2

First add the units $3 + 9 = 12$

Write the 2 in the units column 'carry' the 1 ten into the tens column

Then add the tens $2 + 4 + 1$ 'carry' $= 7$

Then add the hundreds $5 + 1 = 6$

Exercise 2E

Copy and complete:

1   1 4 7
 + 3 3 5

2   2 7 6
 + 4 1 9

3   3 1 4
 + 2 1 9

4   5 1 2
 + 1 7 8

5   6 1 8
 + 2 4 3

6   1 1 7
 + 2 4 6

7   7 5 5
 + 1 3 8

8   6 2 5
 + 1 3 6

9   4 7 3
 + 1 1 9

10   1 6 7
 + 7 2 7

Example

Complete

```
  H T U
  1 5 2
+ 4 4 9
-------
```

Answer:

```
  H T U
  1 5 2
+ 4₁ 4₁ 9
-------
  6 0 1
```

Adding the units:
2 + 9 = 11

Adding the tens:
5 + 4 + 1 'carry' = 10

Adding the hundreds:
1 + 4 + 1 'carry' = 6

Exercise 2F

Copy and complete:

1 6 4 7
     + 1 6 7

2 7 8 5
     + 1 7 6

3 2 6 9
     + 1 7 5

4 3 6 8
     + 1 5 9

5 4 7 7
     + 1 6 5

6 3 7 8
     + 2 7 8

7 2 9 5
     + 1 8 6

8 3 6 9
     + 3 7 4

9 5 8 4
     + 1 9 8

10 3 4 4
     + 1 8 7

Remember

To add two numbers:

1. Write the numbers in H, T, U columns.
2. Add the units.
3. Add the tens.
4. Add the hundreds.
5. Carry to the next column when the number is 10 or more.

3 Subtraction

You can subtract numbers using cubes or a number line.
Every addition sum has 2 subtractions go with it.

When you know the pairs of numbers that add to 20 you
can use them to work out the subtractions that go with them.

For example, $17 + 3 = 20$ Using cubes:
so $20 - 3 = 17$
and $20 - 17 = 3$

20) take away
3

leaves 17

Example

Work out $20 - 4$

$16 + 4 = 20$ Answer: $20 - 4 = 16$

Exercise 3A

Work out:

a $20 - 7$ **b** $20 - 2$ **c** $20 - 10$ **d** $20 - 5$

When you subtract numbers, put them into H, T, U columns first.

Example

Complete   H T U   Answer: H T U
              5 4   5 4
           − 2 3   − 2 3
           _____   _____
                                    3 1

$5 - 2 = 3$ $4 - 3 = 1$

5 tens   4 units
take away
2 tens 3 units

leaves 3 tens 1 unit

Exercise 3B

Copy and complete:

1   **a** H T U   **b** H T U   **c** H T U   **d** H T U
              3 7   4 5   3 4   6 4
           − 2 1   − 1 2   − 2 1   − 1 1
           _____   _____   _____   _____

2   Check your answers with a calculator.

Splitting 10s

You can subtract larger numbers in the same way.
First write the numbers in H, T, U columns.

Example

Complete

```
  H  T  U
  4  7  8
- 1  3  4
  _____
```

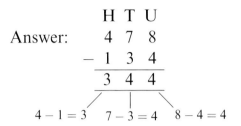

Answer:

```
   H  T  U
   4  7  8
-  1  3  4
   _____
   3  4  4
```

4 − 1 = 3   7 − 3 = 4   8 − 4 = 4

Exercise 3C

Copy and complete:

1

a
```
  H  T  U
  3  7  5
- 2  1  4
  _____
```

b
```
  H  T  U
  5  6  8
- 2  1  3
  _____
```

c
```
  H  T  U
  4  6  7
- 3  1  1
  _____
```

d
```
  H  T  U
  8  5  4
- 4  3  1
  _____
```

e
```
  H  T  U
  5  4  7
- 2  2  5
  _____
```

Sometimes you can't 'take away' the units. For example, 72 − 37

```
  H  T  U
     7  2
-    3  7
  _____
```
— 2 − 7: you can't do this,

Using cubes:

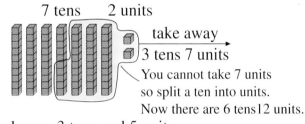

7 tens   2 units

take away
3 tens 7 units

You cannot take 7 units
so split a ten into units.
Now there are 6 tens 12 units.

You have to split one of
the 10s into units

leaves 3 tens and 5 units

Split a ten
to make 10 units.

Now there are 6 tens
and 12 units.

```
  H   T   U
      ₆7  ¹2
-     3   7
  _____
      3   5
```

12 units − 7 units = 5 units

6 tens − 3 tens = 3 tens

Exercise 3D

Copy and complete:

1

a
```
  H  T  U
     4  3
-    2  7
  _____
```

b
```
  H  T  U
     5  4
-    1  9
  _____
```

c
```
  H  T  U
     3  2
-    1  7
  _____
```

d
```
  H  T  U
     6  4
-    2  5
  _____
```

e
```
  H  T  U
     4  1
-    2  3
  _____
```

You use the same method with larger numbers.

Take away 158 from 584

Using cubes:

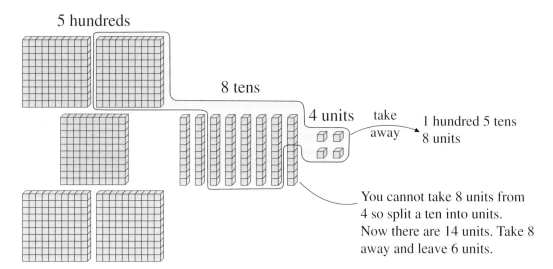

5 hundreds

8 tens

4 units   take away   → 1 hundred 5 tens 8 units

You cannot take 8 units from 4 so split a ten into units. Now there are 14 units. Take 8 away and leave 6 units.

leaves 4 hundreds 2 tens and 6 units

Split a ten to make 10 units
Now there are 7 tens and 14 units.

```
  H T U
  5 8⁷ ⁱ4
− 1 5 8
  4 2 6
```

14 units – 8 units = 6 units

7 tens – 5 tens = 2 tens

5 hundreds – 1 hundred = 4 hundreds

Example

Complete
```
  H T U
  6 7 3
− 2 3 7
```

Answer:
```
  H T U
  6 ⁷⁶ ⁱ3
− 2 3 7
  4 3 6
```

Cannot take 7 units from 3 units so split a ten
13 units – 7 units = 6 units

Exercise 3E

Copy and complete:

1

a
```
  H T U
  5 8 4
− 1 3 8
```

b
```
  H T U
  5 7 2
− 1 4 7
```

c
```
  H T U
  7 7 3
− 1 1 5
```

d
```
  H T U
  3 3 5
− 1 1 7
```

e
```
  H T U
  5 3 4
− 2 1 5
```

Splitting 100s

Sometimes you have to split a hundred into 10s.

523 take away 252   Using cubes:

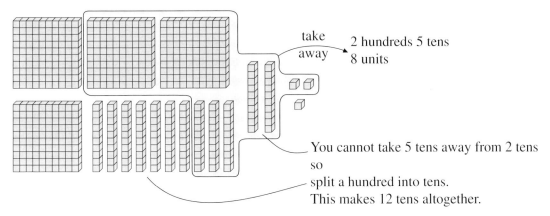

take away   2 hundreds 5 tens
8 units

You cannot take 5 tens away from 2 tens
so
split a hundred into tens.
This makes 12 tens altogether.

leaves 2 hundreds 7 tens and 1 unit

You write:

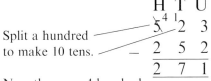

```
      H  T  U
      ⁴  ¹
      5̸  2  3
   −  2  5  2
   _____
      2  7  1
```

Split a hundred
to make 10 tens.

Now there are 4 hundreds
and 12 tens.

Example

Complete

```
   H  T  U
   4  4  8
−  2  5  4
_____
```

Answer:

```
    H  T  U
    ³ ¹
   4̸4  8
−  2  5  4
_____
   1  9  4
```

Cannot take 5 tens from 4 tens
so split a hundred
Units $8 - 4 = 4$
Tens $14 - 5 = 9$
Hundreds $3 - 2 = 1$

Exercise 3F

Copy and complete:

1 **a**
```
   H  T  U
   4  5  7
−  2  8  4
_____
```
b
```
   H  T  U
   5  3  6
−  2  6  2
_____
```
c
```
   H  T  U
   7  1  9
−  5  3  4
_____
```
d
```
   H  T  U
   4  4  3
−  1  7  2
_____
```
e
```
   H  T  U
   6  3  5
−  2  6  4
_____
```

Sometimes you will need to split 10s and 100s in the same sum.

532 take away 256   Using cubes:

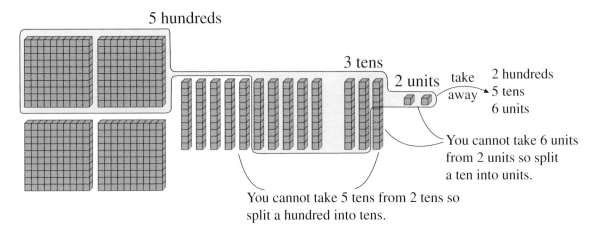

5 hundreds

3 tens

2 units   take away   2 hundreds
5 tens
6 units

You cannot take 6 units from 2 units so split a ten into units.

You cannot take 5 tens from 2 tens so split a hundred into tens.

leaves 2 hundreds 7 tens 6 units

```
  H  T  U
  5⁴ ¹3² ¹2
- 2  5  6
  2  7  6
```

Units: cannot take 6 from 2 so split a ten.
Now there are 2 tens and 12 units. Take 6 from 12

Tens: cannot take 5 from 2 so split a hundred.
Now there are 4 hundreds and 12 tens. Take 5 from 12

Hundreds: take 2 from 4

Example

Complete
```
  H  T  U
  4  2  5
- 1  7  8
```

Answer:
```
  H  T  U
  4³ ²2¹ ¹5
- 1  7  8
  2  4  7
```

Units: cannot take 8 from 5 so split a ten. Take 8 from 15
$15 - 8 = 7$

Tens: cannot take 7 from 1 so split a hundred. Take 7 from 11
$11 - 7 = 4$

Hundreds: take 1 from 3
$3 - 1 = 2$

Exercise 3G

Copy and complete:

1
a
```
  H  T  U
  3  4  5
- 1  6  7
```
b
```
  H  T  U
  5  1  4
- 2  4  7
```
c
```
  H  T  U
  7  2  5
- 3  7  8
```
d
```
  H  T  U
  8  1  4
- 4  3  6
```
e
```
  H  T  U
  9  4  2
- 4  6  7
```

Remember   Always take away Units first, then Tens, then Hundreds.

4 Symmetry

A lot of shapes have symmetry. This means you can divide the shape into two equal parts and each part is a reflection of the other.

You will need a mirror.

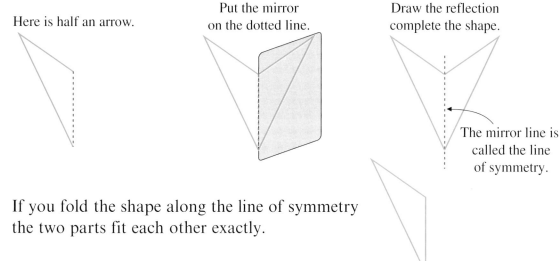

Here is half an arrow.

Put the mirror on the dotted line.

Draw the reflection complete the shape.

The mirror line is called the line of symmetry.

If you fold the shape along the line of symmetry the two parts fit each other exactly.

Example

Copy the shapes and lines of symmetry.

Put your mirror on the dotted line. Draw in the rest of the shape to complete it.

Answer:

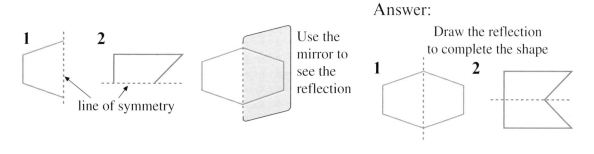

1   2

line of symmetry

Use the mirror to see the reflection

Draw the reflection to complete the shape

1   2

Exercise 4A

Copy the shapes and lines of symmetry. Put your mirror on the dotted line. Draw in the rest of the shape to complete it.

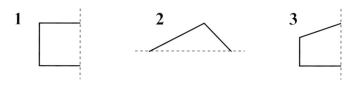

1   2   3

You can use a mirror to help you find the line of symmetry.

Try the mirror on the shape until the reflection looks like the original shape.

Test these with your mirror.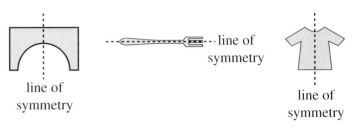

The line of symmetry divides the shape into two equal parts – so it is always near the middle of a shape.

Example

Copy this shape.
Find its line of symmetry.

First copy the shape.

Guess where the line of symmetry might be – draw it in pencil.

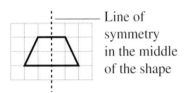

Test with your mirror on the line you have drawn.

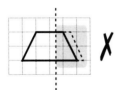 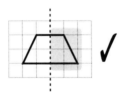

The reflection in the mirror does not complete the shape. Try drawing another line

The reflection in the mirror completes the shape – the line of symmetry is correct

Answer:

Exercise 4B

Copy each shape. Draw the line of symmetry.

Use a mirror to help you.

1  2   3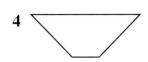

4   5 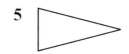 6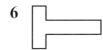

Some shapes have more than one line of symmetry.
Some have none.

This shape has two lines of symmetry.   This shape has no lines of symmetry.

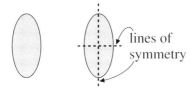   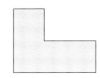

lines of
symmetry

Check with your mirror.   Check with your mirror.

Example

How many lines of symmetry has each shape?

1   2

Use your mirror across the shape in different directions.

Remember that each line of symmetry goes through the
middle of the shape.

1   Answer: 3   2   Wherever you
put the mirror
the reflection does
not complete the
shape.   Answer: 0

Exercise 4C

Use your mirror.

How many lines of symmetry has each shape?

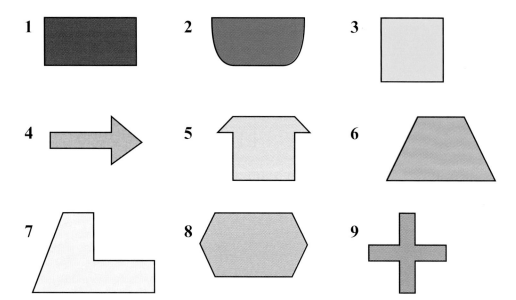

1   2   3

4   5   6

7   8   9

Remember

When you fold the shape on the line of symmetry it fits exactly.

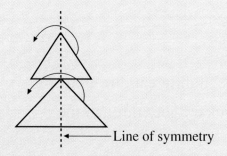

Line of symmetry

The line of symmetry goes through the middle of the shape.

5 Rectangles and squares

Rectangles and squares have 4 sides and 4 right angles.

Rectangle

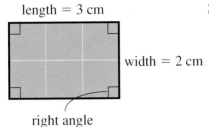

length = 3 cm

width = 2 cm

right angle

Square

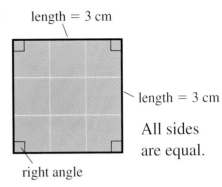

length = 3 cm

length = 3 cm

All sides are equal.

right angle

Example

For this shape, find:

a   the length   **b**   the width.

c   Write the name of the shape.

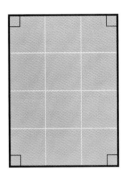

a   Count the squares on a longer side for the length.
    Answer: 4 cm

b   Count the squares on a shorter side for the width.
    Answer: 3 cm

c   Answer: rectangle

Exercise 5A

For each shape, find: **a** the length **b** the width. **c** Write the name of the shape.

1    **2** 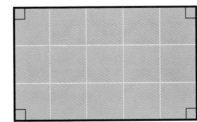   **3**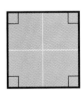

4    **5** 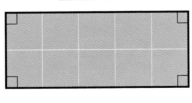   **6**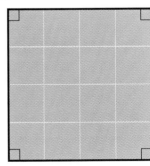

Sometimes you are asked to draw a rectangle. You are given the length and width.

Example

Draw a rectangle with length = 4 cm, width = 3 cm.

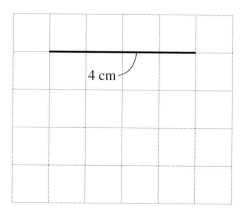

1 Use a ruler to draw a line 4 cm long for the length.

2 Draw two 3 cm lines at right angles.

3 Draw another 4 cm line to complete the rectangle.

Use a ruler to draw all the lines.

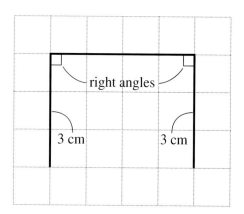

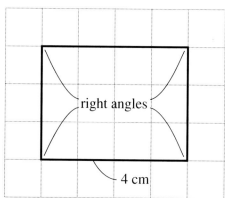

Exercise 5B

You need squared paper and a ruler.

1 Draw a rectangle with length = 5 cm, width = 4 cm.

2 Draw a square with length = 4 cm. ——————— In a square width is the same as length.

3 Draw a square with length = 5 cm.

4 Draw a rectangle with length = 7 cm, width = 2 cm.

5 Draw a rectangle with length = 10 cm, width = 5 cm.

6 Draw a square with length = 7 cm.

7 Draw a square with length 2 cm.

8 Draw a rectangle with length = 6 cm, width = 2 cm.

Example

Find the distance all round the shape.

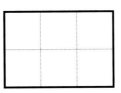

1 Find the length and width:
length 3 cm, width 2 cm

2 All around the shape is: length + width + length + width

3 Write the sum and find the total: $3 + 2 + 3 + 2 = 10$ cm

Answer: 10 cm

Example

Find the distance all round each shape.

a Rectangle with length 5 cm, width 4 cm
All around the shape is length + width + length + width
$5 + 4 + 5 + 4 = 18$ cm

Answer: 8 cm

b Square with length 6 cm
All around the shape is length + width + length + width
$6 + 6 + 6 + 6 = 24$ cm

Answer: 24 cm

> In a square length and width are *the same*.

Exercise 5C

Find the distance all the way around each shape.

1
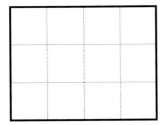

2
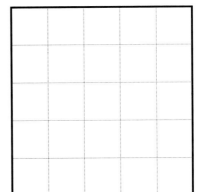

3 Rectangle with length = 8 cm,
width = 4 cm

4 Rectangle with length = 10 cm,
width = 5 cm

5 Square with length = 5 cm

6 Square with length = 8 cm

6 Pictograms

A pictogram shows information in a table.

To show numbers of objects on a pictogram you use symbols.

For example, for 25 people you could draw

To save time and space you could say that = 5 people.

Then you only have to draw

This represents 25 people.

A symbol like = 5 people, is called a **key**.

Example

 = 10 drinks

Show how you would draw 50 drinks.

Answer:
Count: 10   20   30   40   50

Exercise 6A

1   = 5 ice creams.

   Show how you would draw 20 ice creams.

2   = 2 people.

   Show how you would draw 10 people.

3   = 4 cars.

   Show how you would draw 12 cars.

Drawing pictograms

Example

Draw a pictogram to show how people spend their day out.

  25 go to the country
  10 go to the seaside
  15 go to the park

Use 👤 = 5 people.

Answer: Work out the number of symbols for country,

    25 people =

    Count: 5 10 15 20 25

  seaside, 10 people =

    Count: 5 10

  park, 15 people =

    Count: 5 10 15

Then draw the pictogram.

How people spend their day	
country	👤👤👤👤👤
seaside	👤👤
park	👤👤👤

Exercise 6B

1 Copy and complete this pictogram to show the vehicles in a car park.

  12 vans
  16 cars
   8 mini buses

 Use ⬛ = 4 vehicles.

Vehicles in a car park	
vans	
cars	
minibuses	

2   Draw a pictogram to show the drinks sold at break.

> 50 orange
> 20 blackcurrent
> 25 lemonade

Use 🥛 = 10 drinks

Copy and complete:

Drinks sold at break	
orange	
blackcurrant	
lemonade	

3   Draw a pictogram to show the cakes sold at lunchtime.

> chocolate 80
> doughnuts 60
> flapjacks   70
> cream   10

Use 😊 = 20 cakes

Copy and complete:

Cakes sold at lunchtime	
chocolate	
doughnuts	
flapjacks	
cream	

Reading pictograms

When information is given in a pictogram you use the key to work out what the symbols show.

Example

This pictogram shows the number of books of 1st and 2nd class stamps sold at the Post Office.

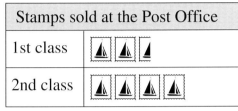

Key: ◮ = 20 books
of stamps

a How many were 1st class books?
b How many were 2nd class books?

a

20 20 10
◮ ◮ ◮ ← This is half of ◮
Count: 20 40 50 Half of 20 is 10.

Answer: 50

b

20 20 20 20
◮ ◮ ◮ ◮
Count: 20 40 60 80

Answer: 80

Exercise 6C

1

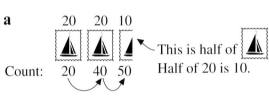

Key: ⬙ = 20 drinks

The pictogram shows the drinks sold in the canteen.

a How many teas were sold?
b How many orange were sold?

2

Letters received	
Monday	✉ ✉
Tuesday	✉ ◺
Wednesday	✉ ✉ ◺
Thursday	✉ ✉ ✉
Friday	✉ ✉
Saturday	✉

Key: ✉ = 10 letters

a How many letters were received on Tuesday?
b How many letters were received on Wednesday?
c How many letters were received on Friday?

3

Key: 🧍 = 20 pupils
🧍 = 10 pupils
🧍 = 5 pupils

How many pupils went each day?

Sometimes you are asked questions about the most popular or least popular objects.

Example

Favourite dinners	
roast	⊙⊙⊙⊙
curry	⊙⊙
pie	⊙◖
spaghetti	⊙⊙⊙
pizza	⊙⊙⊙◖

Key: ⊙ = 10 people

1   Which dinner is most popular? ⟍ 'most popular' means the most people chose it

2   Which dinner is least popular? — 'least popular' means the smallest number chose it

3   How many people were asked?

Answer:

1   Roast is most popular.   2   Pie is least popular.

3   Total asked = roast + curry + pie + spaghetti + pizza
$$= 40 + 20 + 15 + 30 + 35$$
So 140 people were asked.

Exercise 6D

1

Drinks sold	
tea	🥤🥤🥤
coffee	🥤🥤🥤
orange	🥤🥤
fizz	🥤🥤🥤

Key: 🥤 = 10 drinks

a   Which drink sold the most?
b   Which drink sold the least?
c   How many drinks were sold altogether?

Remember
Look at the **key**.
It tells you what the symbols mean.

2

Saturday afternoon activity	
TV	웃웃웃
shopping	웃웃
sport	웃웃웃웃
cinema	웃
club	웃웃웃

Key: 웃 = 5 people

a   Which activity is most popular?
b   Which activity is least popular?
c   How many people were asked?

7 Sequences

These numbers follow a pattern.

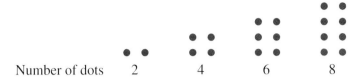

Number of dots   2   4   6   8

The number of dots makes a **sequence** 2, 4, 6, 8.

The seqence grows by adding 2 dots each time.

The next two numbers are:

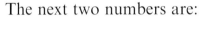

10   12

You **add 2** each time.

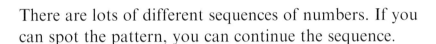

There are lots of different sequences of numbers. If you can spot the pattern, you can continue the sequence.

Example

Copy and write the next two numbers in this sequence.

     3, 5, 7, 9, —, —

Find what you have to add each time.

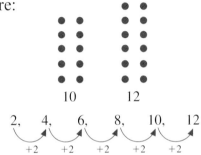

The sequence grows by adding 2.

Answer: 3, 5, 7, 9, <u>11</u>, <u>13</u>

$9 + 2 = 11$
$11 + 2 = 13$

Exercise 7A

Copy and write the next two numbers in the sequences.

1   3, 6, 9, 12, __, __.   **2**   6, 7, 8, 9, __.

3   5, 10, 15, 20, __, __.   **4**   10, 20, 30, 40, __, __.

5   100, 200, 300, __, __.   **6**   110, 120, 130, __, __.

Sometimes you have to find missing numbers in a sequence.

You need to find what you have to add each time.

Example

Copy and fill in the missing numbers:

6, 8, 10, __, 14, 16, __,

Answer:
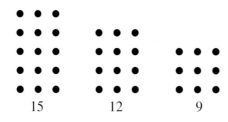
6, 8, 10, 12, 14, 16, 18   You add 2 each time.
+2 +2 +2 +2 +2 +2

Exercise 7B

Copy and fill in the missing numbers.

a 4, 5, __, 7, 8.
b 15, 16, __, 18, 19.
c 50, 60, 70, __, 90, 100.
d 25, 30, __, 40, 45, 50.
e 3, 6, 9, 12, __, 18, __.

These dot patterns make a sequence:

Number of dots   15   12   9

The numbers are getting smaller each time.

The sequence 15, 12, 9 does down by 3 each time.
To find the next number take away 3.

The next two numbers are
6   3

This sequence is
15 12 9 6 3
−3 −3 −3 −3

Example

Copy and write the next two numbers.

    20, 18, 16, 14, —, —

Find what you have to take away.

Answer:

$$20, \quad 18, \quad 16, \quad 14, \quad \underline{12}, \quad \underline{10}.$$

$$-2 \quad -2 \quad -2 \quad -2 \quad -2 \qquad 12 - 2 = 10$$

$$14 - 2 = 12$$

Exercise 7C

1   Copy and write the next two numbers.

    a   8, 7, 6, 5, —, —,
    b   19, 17, 15, 13, —, —,
    c   25, 22, 19, 16, —, —,
    d   50, 45, 40, 35, —, —,
    e   600, 500, 400, —, —,

2   Copy and write the next two numbers.
    a   40, 50, 60, 70, —, —,
    b   18, 14, 10, —, —,
    c   100, 110, 120, —, —,
    d   50, 100, 150, 200, —, —,
    e   25, 20, 15, —, —,
    f   50, 48, 46, 44, —, —,
    g   30, 35, 40, 45, —, —,

Remember

Look for the pattern in the sequence.

If the numbers get **bigger**, you **add** something each time.

If the numbers get **smaller**, you **take away** something each time.

8 Journeys

You need to know how to write and draw journeys.

These exercises will give you some practice.

Here is a journey.

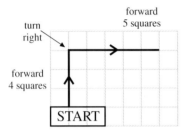

You write this as:
forward 4 squares
turn right
forward 5 squares
stop

Use the words: forward ☐ squares

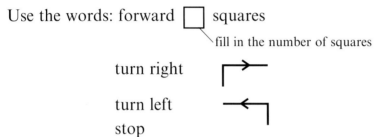

fill in the number of squares

turn right

turn left

stop

Example

Describe this journey.

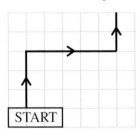

Answer: forward 3 squares
turn right
forward 5 squares
turn left
forward 2 squares
stop

Exercise 8A

Describe these journeys.

1
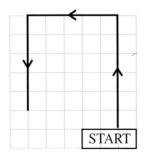

2
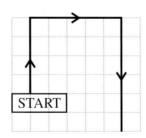

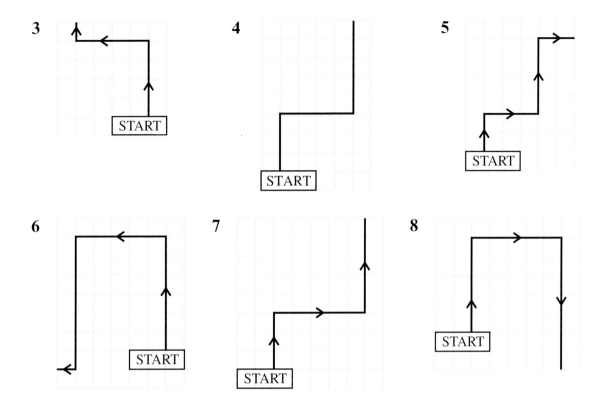

Examples

1   Draw this journey on squared paper:

Answer:

forward 3 squares
turn left
forward 2 squares
turn right
forward 4 squares
stop

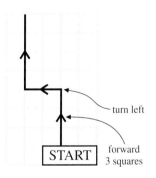

2   Draw this journey on squared paper:

Answer:

forward 2 squares
turn right
forward 3 squares
turn right
forward 6 squares
stop

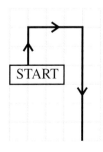

Exercise 8B

Draw these journeys on squared paper:

1   forward 5 squares
    turn right
    forward 6 squares
    turn left
    forward 1 square
    stop

2   forward 3 squares
    turn left
    forward 4 squares
    turn right
    forward 5 squares
    stop

3   forward 4 squares
    turn left
    forward 3 squares
    turn left
    forward 8 squares
    stop

4   forward 6 squares
    turn right
    forward 4 squares
    turn right
    forward 5 squares
    stop

5   forward 1 square
    turn right
    forward 3 squares
    turn left
    forward 2 squares
    turn right
    forward 2 squares
    stop

6   forward 8 squares
    turn left
    forward 8 squares
    turn left
    forward 8 squares
    turn left
    forward 5 squares
    stop

7   forward 7 squares
    turn right
    forward 5 squares
    turn right
    forward 4 squares
    turn left
    forward 6 squares
    stop

8   forward 5 squares
    turn right
    forward 4 squares
    turn left
    forward 7 squares
    turn right
    forward 4 squares
    stop

9 Describe the journey to make this square.

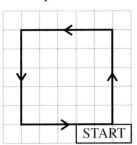

10 Describe the journey to make this rectangle.

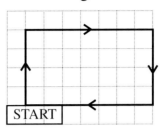

Sometimes you will be asked to match a journey to some instructions.

Example

Which journey follows these instructions?

    forward 3 squares
    turn right
    forward 2 squares
    stop

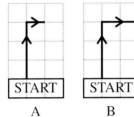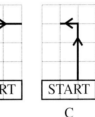

Work through the instructions one at a time and see which journey they fit.

    forward 3 squares ← this fits A, B and C
    turn right   ← this fits A and B
                     (So C is not the answer.)
    forward 2 squares ← this fits B
    stop   (So A is not the answer.)

Answer: B

Exercise 8C

Which journey follows these instructions?

    forward 2 squares
    turn left
    forward 4 squares
    turn right
    forward 1 square
    stop

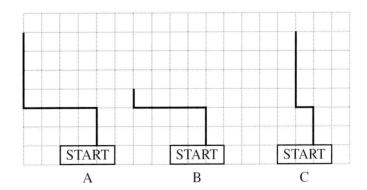

9 Clocks and watches

To tell the time you need to be able to read a clock.

The small hand is
on 5.
The long hand is
on 12.
5 o'clock

The small hand is
between 7 and 8.
The long hand is
on 6.
half past 7

The small hand is
between 12 and 1.
The long hand is
on 3.
quarter past 12

The small hand is
between 5 and 6.
The long hand is
on 9.
quarter to 6

Example

Write the times on these clocks.

  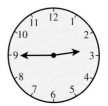

Answer: 9 o'clock   quarter past 8   quarter to 3

Exercise 9A

Write the times on these clocks.

1    **2** 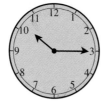   **3**

4    **5**    **6**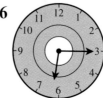

Counting the minutes

It takes the long hand 1 hour to go all round the clock.

1 hour = 60 minutes
There are 5 minutes in each gap.

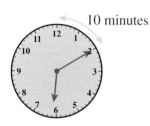

10 minutes

35 minutes

10 minutes past 6
or 6:10

35 minutes past 10
or 10:35——You write this for short

5 o'clock
or 5:00

quarter past 7
or 7:15

half past 2
or 2:30

quarter to 1
or 12:45

Example

Write the times on these clocks.

25 minutes

55 minutes

Answer: 2:25

the short hand   the long hand

3:55

You can say 3:55 as '5 minutes to 4', because when the long hand has moved 5 minutes it will be 4 o'clock.

It is quicker to write 3:55.

Exercise 9B

Write the times on these clocks.

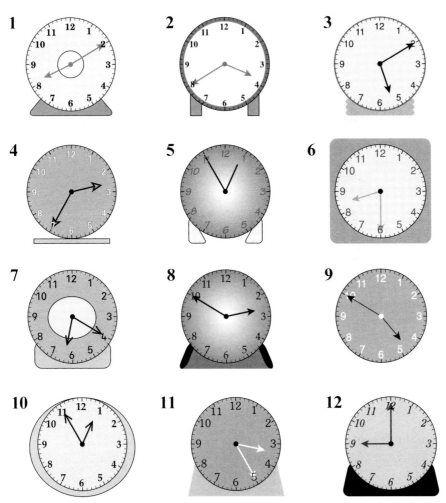

Digital clocks and watches

These show the time using numbers, the same way as you write times 'for short'.

4:25

10:44

In words: four twenty five

In words: ten forty four

Example

Write the time: **a** in numbers
                b in words

Answer: **a** 3:26 **b** three twenty six

Exercise 9C

Write the time: **a** in numbers
                b in words

1   2   3   4 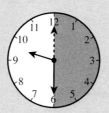 5 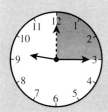 6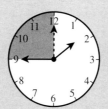

Remember
From 9 o'clock
the long hand has gone
half way round.
It is **half past 9**.

From 9 o'clock
the long hand has
gone a **quarter** way
round.
It is **quarter past 9**.

The long hand has
to go a **quarter** way
round to reach
2 o'clock.
It is **quarter to 2**.

7:30 is the same as 'half past 7'

8:00 is the same as '8 o'clock'

10 Time lines

A time line is a plan that shows the times things happen.

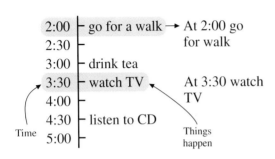

Another timeline:

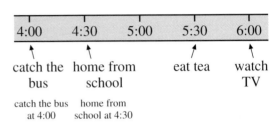

Example

Joe's time line

8:00 ├ eat breakfast
9:00 ├ jog
10:00 ├ shower
11:00 ├ read

1 What does Joe do at   **a**   9:00
                                          b   11:00?
2 What time does Joe eat breakfast?

1 **a** Look at 9:00 on the time line.

    Answer: jog

  b Answer: read

2 Look at 'eat breakfast' on the time line. Read across to the time.

  Answer: 8:00

Exercise 10A

1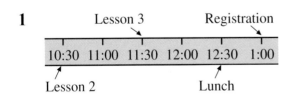

    a What happens at 12:30?
    b What happens at 10:30?
    c What time is registration?

2

6:30	homework
7:00	coffee
7:30	computer
8:00	TV

    a What happens at 8:00?
    b What time is coffee?
    c What happens at 7:30?

3 Copy this time line.

5:00	5:30	6:00	6:30	7:00	7:30	8:00	8:30

Put these on your time line.
6:30 football, 8:00 badminton, 6:00 netball, 5:00 hockey,
8:30 basketball, 7:00 swimming

Time intervals

Time lines can show how long something takes.

A TV programme begins at 5:00.
It ends at 6:00.
From 5:00 to 6:00 is 1 hour.
The programme lasts 1 hour.

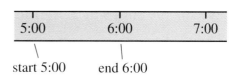

Homework begins at 6:30
It ends at 8:30.

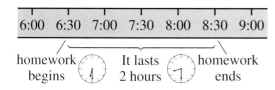

A lesson begins at 9:30
It ends at 10:00.

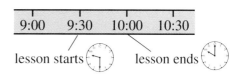

Examples

1 I eat lunch from 12:30 to 1:00
How long do I take?

Write the times on a time line.

Answer: 30 minutes

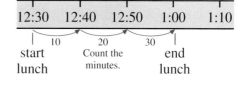

2 I play basketball from 2:10 to 2:50
How long do I play?

Write the times between 2:10 and 2:50.

I play basketball for 40 minutes.

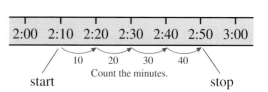

Exercise 10B

How long do these last?

1   The London Marathon starts at 9:30. I finish at 12:30.

2   I leave for school at 8:20. I arrive at school at 8:40.

3   A car journey begins at 3:20. It ends at 4:20.

4   The disco starts at 8:00. It ends at 10:00.

5   I go shopping from 10:00 to 2:00.

6   School starts at 9:00. It ends at 3:00.

7   I leave for the shops at 3:30. I arrive home at 3:55.

8   The flight from London Gatwick to Newcastle leaves at 10:10, arrives at 10:50.

Minutes and seconds

Minutes are divided into seconds.
1 minute = 60 seconds
It takes 1 second to say 'one elephant'.

Some activities last for seconds.
To run 100 metres:
Estimate how long.
About 20 seconds

Some activities take minutes.
To make a sandwich:
Estimate how long.
About 3 minutes.

Exercise 10C

About how long for these? Use minutes or seconds.

1   Make a phone call

2   Boil an egg

3   Read a newspaper

4   Clean your teeth

5   Morning break at school

6   Make a cup of tea

7   Take a shower

8   Do one homework

11 Fraction parts

To describe how much of a shape is shaded
You need to use fractions.

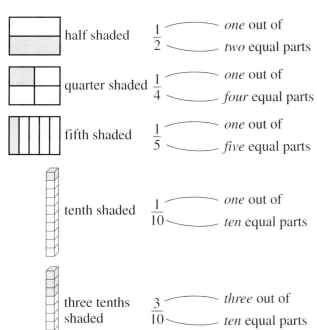

Example

Shade $\frac{3}{5}$ of the shape.

Answer: $\frac{3}{5}$ ⌒ Shade 3 out of
5 equal parts

Exercise 11A

Copy and complete:

a   Shade $\frac{3}{4}$ of

b   Shade $\frac{2}{5}$ of

c   Shade $\frac{1}{6}$ of

d   Shade $\frac{7}{10}$ of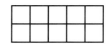

e   Shade $\frac{1}{8}$ of

f   Shade $\frac{1}{9}$ of

Example

What fraction is blue?

First count the number of equal parts.
Then count the blue parts.

There are 10 equal parts, 3 are blue:

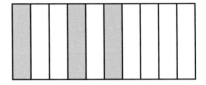

Answer: $\frac{3}{10}$

Exercise 11B

What fraction is blue?

a   b   c 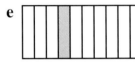   d   e

f   g   h   i   j

You can divide circles into fractions in the same way.

Example

What fraction is red?

First count the number of equal parts.
Then count the red parts.

There are 5 equal parts, 2 are red:

Answer: $\frac{2}{5}$

Exercise 11C

What fraction is red?

a   b   c   d   e

f   g   h   i   j

Drawing fractions

Sometimes you are asked to draw a shape and shade a fraction.

Example

Draw a shape and shade $\frac{3}{8}$.

Draw any shape with 8 **equal** parts.
Shade **any** 3 parts.

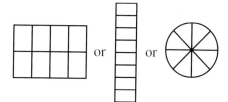

Answer: 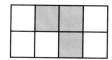   There are lots of possible answers.

Exercise 11D

Draw some shapes of your own and shade these fractions:

a $\frac{3}{4}$ b $\frac{2}{5}$ c $\frac{3}{10}$ d $\frac{4}{5}$ e $\frac{9}{10}$ f $\frac{1}{4}$ g $\frac{7}{10}$

Missing parts

Example

How much of this chocolate bar has been eaten?

There were 21 parts altogether (count them).

5 have been eaten.

Answer: $\frac{5}{21}$

Exercise 11E

1   How much of this cake has been eaten?

2   How much of this pizza is left?

3   How much of this chocolate bar has been eaten?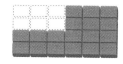

Sometimes the shape is not divided into the number of parts you want.

Example

Shade $\frac{3}{5}$ of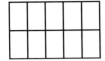

There are 10 parts but we need 5 equal parts.

Think of the shape as 5 of these:

Shade any 3 of them.

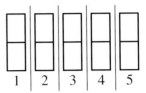

The 10 parts are split into 5.

Answer:

Exercise 11F

Copy and complete:

1   Shade $\frac{1}{2}$ of

2   Shade $\frac{3}{4}$ of

3   Shade $\frac{1}{5}$ of

4   Shade $\frac{1}{6}$ of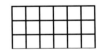

Remember
Count the equal parts.
Write the number on the bottom.
Write the number of shaded parts on top.

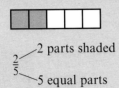

2 parts shaded

$\frac{2}{5}$

5 equal parts

12 Money, money, money

You use money every day. This page shows you how to read and write amounts of money.

$= 115\text{p}$ $= 115\text{p}$

$= 100\text{p} = £1$

$= 115\text{p}$ we say 'one hundred and fifteen pence'

is the same as

$= £1.15$ we say 'one pound 15p'

$115\text{p} = £1.15$

Example

Write 324 pence in pounds.

Each hundred pence is one pound so 324p is 3 pounds 24p.

Answer: £3.24

Exercise 12A

Write these pence in pounds.

a	135p	b	152p	c	172p	d	275p	e	210p
f	109p	g	102p	h	203p	i	199p	j	200p

Money on a calculator

When you buy several items you need to **add** the prices to find the **total cost**. You can use a calculator.

Use a calculator to work out   27p + 43p + 38p

Write the answer using £.

Key in ② ⑦ ⊞ ④ ③ ⊞ ③ ⑧ ⊟   _108._

Answer: Write in £: £1.08

Exercise 12B

Use a calculator to work these out. Write the answer using £.

a 72p + 43p	**b** 32p + 55p + 28p	**c** 93p + 33p + 41p
d 89p + 51p	**e** 97p + 64p	**f** 72p + 55p + 33p
g 23p + 5p + 82p	**h** 95p + 85p + 15p	**i** 48p + 50p + 78p
j 99p + 87p + 3p	**k** 37p + 42p + 97p	**l** 5p + 20p + 89p

Writing money in pence

Sometimes you are given an amount in pounds and asked to write it in pence.

Example

Write these in pence   **a** £1.69   **b** £1.04

a   £1.69

£1 is 100p   and   .69 is 69p
100p + 69p is 169p

b   £1.04

£1 is 100p   and   .04 is 4p
100p + 4p is 104p

Answer: **a** 169p   **b** 104p

Exercise 12C

Write these in pence:

1   **a**   £1.32   **b**   £1.74   **c**   £1.59   **d**   £1.95   **e**   £1.46

2   **a**   £1.09   **b**   £1.05   **c**   £1.08   **d**   £1.02   **e**   £1.01

3   **a**   £2.52   **b**   £2.34   **c**   £2.07   **d**   £2.00   **e**   £3.05

Writing money in pounds

Sometimes amounts less than £1 are written with a £ sign.

0 pounds

50p can also be written £0.50 — 50p

20p can also be written £0.20

Example

Write 75p in pounds.

There are 0 pounds and 75p.
£0 and 75p is £0.75

Answer: £0.75

Exercise 12D

Write these pence in pounds.

a   25p   **b**   90p   **c**   55p   **d**   10p   **e**   5p

Total costs

How much will these cost altogether?

To find the total cost of Starlite, video
and crisps use a calculator to do
£1.85 + £7.99 + £0.28 ——— *All* the money must be in £.

Press   1 . 8 5 + 7 . 9 9 + 0 . 2 8 =   10.12

Total   £10.12

Example

Remember 37p is £0.37

Use a calculator to work out £1.42 + £1.47 + 37p

First write all the money in £.

£1.42 + £1.47 + £0.37

Press   1 · 4 2 + 1 · 4 7 + 0 · 3 7 =   3.26

Answer: £3.26

Exercise 12E

1   Use a calculator to work out the total.   Write the amounts in £ first.
    Write your answer in pounds.

a	£1.50 + £1.04 + 58p	b	£1.42 + £1.30 + 82p
c	£1.04 + 40p + 5p	d	£2.75 + £1.30 + 60p
e	£1.49 + 58p + £1.01	f	£1.72 + 39p + £1.64
g	£1.39 + £2.99 + 82p	h	£1.04 + 67p + 12p
i	9p + £1.52 + 67p	j	£1.68 + 32p + 50p
k	£1.11 + 88p + 9p	l	£1.72 + £1.40 + 18p
m	£1.43 + £2.25 + 74p	n	£1.05 + £2.43 + 19p
o	£1.14 + £2.01 + 70p	p	£1.18 + 47p + 8p

2   Write your answers to question **1** in pence.

Remember

£1.23

These are the pounds.   These are the pence.

£1 = 100p (so £1.23 = 123p).

25p is 0 pounds and 25 pence

So 25p is   £0.25

When you add money amounts write them all in £.
The answer will be in £.

13 Measures

Length

Length and distance are measured in these units:

centimetres   short form: cm
metres   short form: m
kilometres   short form: km

You need to be able to estimate length and distance using these units.
Here are some estimates of length.

The length of this
book is about 25 cm.

The height of a
door is about 2 m.

Twice round the
edge of a football
pitch is about 1 km.

Example

Estimate the length of the minibus in the picture.

First find a measurement you know.

The height of the man is about 2 m.

Now compare the minibus and the man.
The minibus is about 2 times as long.
So the minibus is about $2 \times 2\,m = 4\,m$

Answer: 4 m

Exercise 13A

Look at the picture.
Estimate:

a   the height of the garden shed
b   the width of the garage
c   the height of the tree
d   the height of the table
e   the length of the house
f   the height of the house

Choosing units of measure

When you measure something you
need to choose the best units to use.
It would take a long time to measure
a tennis court in cm.

When you are asked to choose a
possible measurement, look at the **units**.

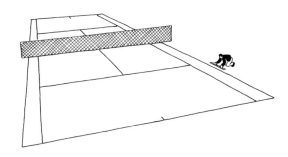

Example

Which measurement could be the length of a pencil?

   a   14 m   **b**   14 cm   **c**   14 km

Answer: **b**

Remember:
a man is about 2 m tall
a book is about 25 cm long
twice round a football pitch
is about 1 km

Example

Which is the best unit to measure
the height of a tree?

Answer: metres.

A tree is less than 1 km tall.
It is hundreds of cm tall.

Exercise 13B

1   Which measurement could be the height of the tree?

   a   15 m
   b   15 km
   c   15 cm

2   Which measurement could be the distance from London to
Birmingham?

   a   190 km
   b   190 cm
   c   190 m

3   Which measurement could be the width of the clock?

   a   20 km
   b   20 m
   c   20 cm

4 Write down the best units to measure these lengths.
Choose from cm, m, or km.

a The height of a house   **b** The distance from Bristol to Newcastle
c The height of a milk bottle **d** The height of a baby
e The width of a classroom   **f** The width of a table
g The length of a pen

Weight (Mass)

Weight is measured in grams   short form: g
           and kilograms   short form: kg

You will need to be able to estimate using these units.
Here are some estimates of weight.

A man weighs   A tea bag weighs   A large loaf
about 75 kg   about 3g   weighs about 1 kg

Example

Estimate the weight of 12 apples.

Imagine how the weight compares with a loaf of bread.
Probably 12 apples = 2 loaves about 2 kg

Exercise 13C

Look at the picture.
Write down an estimate of the weight
of the:

a woman   **b** dog
c sugar   **d** egg
e butter   **f** flour
g basin

Capacity

The amount a container holds is called its capacity.
Capacity is measured in litres.

You need to be able to estimate capacity.

Here are some estimates of capacity.

A teapot holds
about 1 litre
of tea.

A watering can
holds about
5 litres of water.

A bucket holds
about 10 litres
of water.

Exercise 13D

Look at the picture.
Write down an estimate of the number of litres each hold.

a	jug	**b**	milk carton
c	barrel	**d**	bottle cola
e	paddling pool	**f**	dog's water bowl
g	watering can		

Remember
To estimate measurements, think of a measurement
you know.

14 Angles 3

On page 98 you saw how a spinner can make quarter turns and half turns.

A quarter turn looks like this:

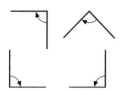

A half turn looks like this:

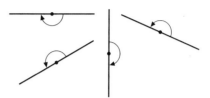

A quarter turn is the corner of this page. A half turn is on a straight line.

Sometimes you will be asked to name quarter turns and half turns.

Examples

1   Which shows a quarter turn?

2   Which shows a half turn?

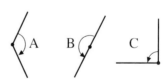

1   Answer: C   It's like the corner of a page.

2   Answer: B   It's on a straight line.

Exercise 14A

1   List the half turns.   2   List the quarter turns.

a   b   c   d   e

f   g   h   i   j

You will need tracing paper.

On page 100 you saw how to turn a shape through an angle.

This pin man
is being turned.

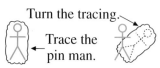

Quarter turn

The pin man has turned through a quarter turn.

Trace

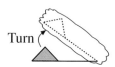

Turn

Turn
further

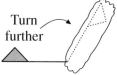

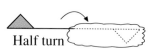

Half turn

The flag has turned through half a turn.

Examples

Are these half turns or quarter turns?

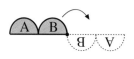

Answer: Half turn   Quarter turn   Quarter turn   Half turn

The pictures are in
a straight line.

Exercise 14B

Are these half turns or quarter turns?
You can use tracing paper to check

1
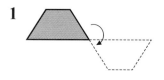

2
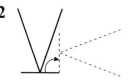

3
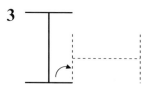

4
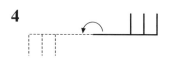

5
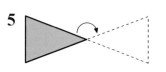

6
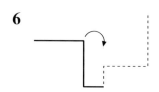

7 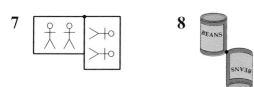 **8**   **9**   **10**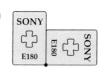

These are right angles.

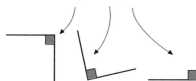

A right angle is a corner of this page.

Examples

How many right angles in each shape?

a **b**

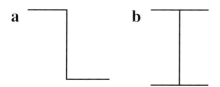

a  Answer: 2   **b**   Answer: 4

Exercise 14C

How many right angles in each shape?

1   **2**   **3** **4**

5 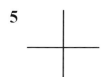 **6** 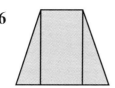 **7**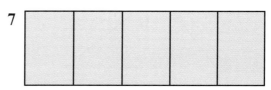

Hint: there are more than 12.

Example

1   List the right angles.

2   List the angles bigger than a right angle.

3   List the angles smaller than a right angle.

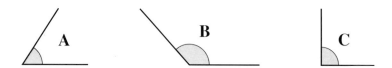

Compare with the corner of a page if you're not sure.

Answer:

1   C a right angle   2   B bigger than a right angle   3 A smaller than a right angle

Exercise 14D

1   List the right angles.

2   List the angles bigger than a right angle.

3   List the angles smaller than a right angle.

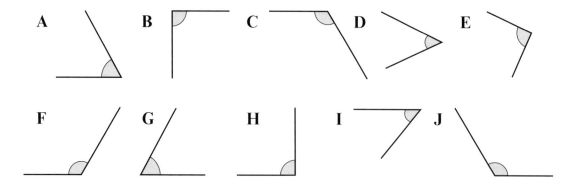

4   **a**   Which angle is biggest?   **b**   Which angle is smallest?

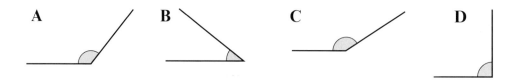

5 **a** Which angle is biggest?
  b Which angle is smallest?

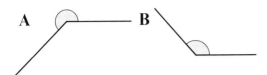 

6 **a** Which angle is biggest?
  b Which angle is smallest?

The angle to look at is marked.

Remember
Quarter turn and right angle

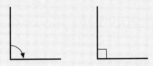

are the same as the corner of a page.

Half turn is on a straight line.

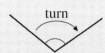 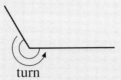

The smallest angle is the smallest turn.
It makes the 'sharpest point'.

15 Reading scales

When you measure amounts accurately you use instruments that have scales.

You need to be able to read measures from different types of scales:

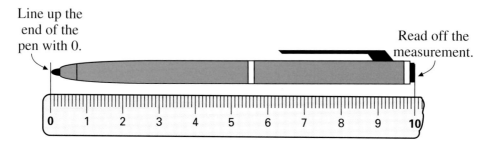

This pen measures 10 cm.

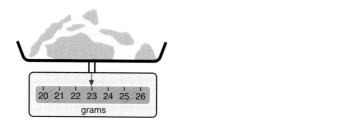

This scale shows 23 grams.

This speedometer shows 60 km/h.

Example

Write down the reading on this scale.

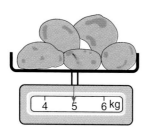

First write the number: 5
Then write the units: kg

Answer: 5 kg

Exercise 15A

Write down the reading shown on these scales.

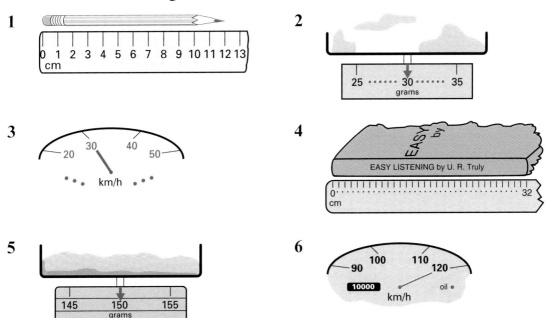

1

2

3

4

5

6

Sometimes the measurement is between two numbers on the scale.

You read the measurements like this.

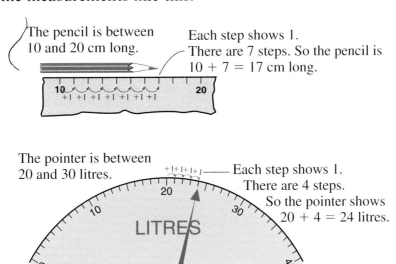

The pencil is between 10 and 20 cm long.

Each step shows 1. There are 7 steps. So the pencil is 10 + 7 = 17 cm long.

The pointer is between 20 and 30 litres.

Each step shows 1. There are 4 steps. So the pointer shows 20 + 4 = 24 litres.

Exercise 15B

What is the reading on each of these scales?

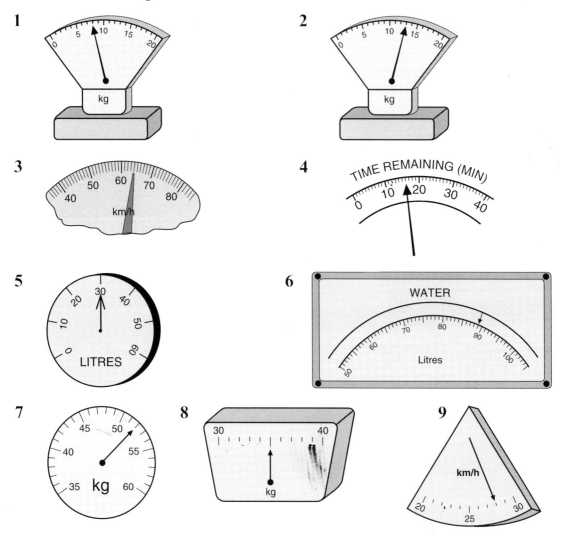

1

2

3

4

5

6

7

8

9

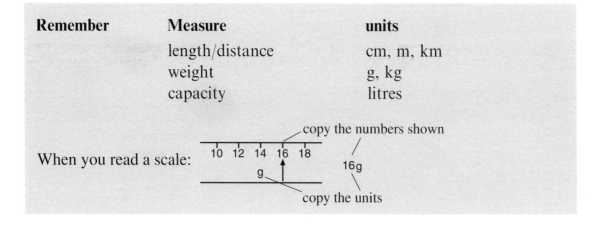

Remember	Measure	units
	length/distance	cm, m, km
	weight	g, kg
	capacity	litres

When you read a scale:

copy the numbers shown

10 12 14 16 18

g

16g

copy the units

16 Colder and colder

Temperature measures how warm or cold something is.
Temperature is measured in degrees centigrade, written °C for short.

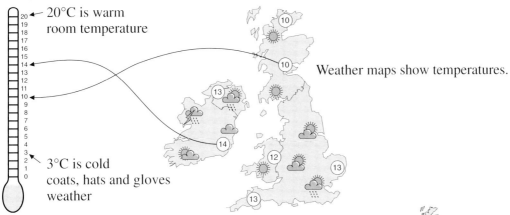

Weather maps show temperatures.

You measure temperature with a thermometer.

A hot day in the UK is 23°C.

A hot day in Spain is 30°C.

Example

Write down the temperature on this thermometer.

Answer: 4°C

The line goes to 4°

Exercise 16A

Write down the temperature on these thermometers.

a  **b**  **c**  **d**

Colder than zero

What happens when temperatures drop below 0°C?

Below 0°C there is frost, ice on puddles, rivers freeze.

A cold day in the UK is 6°C.
A cold day in Russia is −15°C.

Weather forecasters say 'minus 15 degrees' for −15°C.

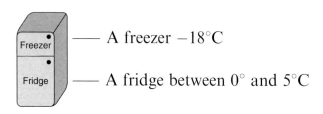

—— A freezer −18°C

—— A fridge between 0° and 5°C

The minus sign shows it is *below* zero.

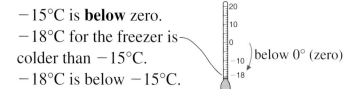

−15°C is **below** zero.
−18°C for the freezer is colder than −15°C.
−18°C is below −15°C.

below 0° (zero)

Example

Write down the temperature on this thermometer.

Answer: −3°C

The line goes to −3°C.

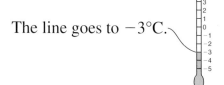

Exercise 16B

Write down the temperatures on these thermometers.

a    b    c    d

Thermometers can also be shown like this:

Example

Write down the temperature on this thermometer.

The line goes to $-2°$.

Answer: $-2°C$

Write down the temperatures shown on these thermometers.

a ![thermometer scale -6 to 2]   b ![thermometer scale -6 to 2]

c ![thermometer scale -6 to 2]   d ![thermometer scale -6 to 2]

Negative numbers

Numbers with a minus sign like $-13°C$ are called **negative numbers**.
Here is a number line like a thermometer scale.

```
  -8  -7  -6  -5  -4  -3  -2  -1   0   1   2   3   4   5
            ←──────────────────
               negative numbers
```

Example

Copy and complete this number line:

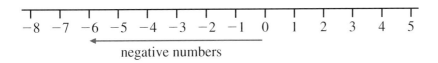

What goes here?

Compare with the number line above.

Answer: $-2 \ -1 \ \ 0 \ \ 1 \ \ 2$

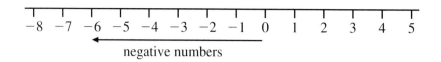

negative numbers

Exercise 16D

Copy and complete these number lines:

Example

What is the missing number?

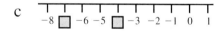

What goes here?

Compare with the number line above.

Answer: -5

Exercise 16E

What are the missing numbers?

a

b

c

Remember

To fill in negative numbers start at 0.

Write from right to left ←

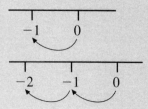

17 Two-way tables

You can use tables to show information.
You need to be able to read information from a table.

For example:

Name	Age	Lunch
John	15	canteen
Sinita	14	packed
Emily	14	packed
Jane	15	canteen

This line shows
'Emily is 14 and has packed lunch'

This table shows the numbers of black and white triangles and squares in a box

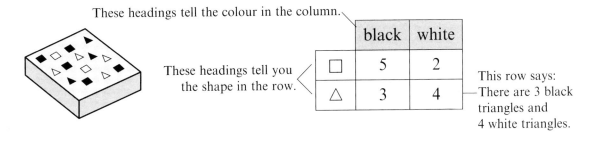

These headings tell the colour in the column.

These headings tell you
the shape in the row.

	black	white
□	5	2
△	3	4

This row says:
There are 3 black
triangles and
4 white triangles.

Example

The table shows how many boys and girls prefer pizza or burgers.

	Boys	Girls
Pizza	7	3
Burgers	5	2

a   How many boys prefer burgers?
b   How many girls prefer pizza?
c   How many people prefer burgers?

Answer:

a   5 boys prefer burgers

b   3 girls prefer pizza

c

	Boys	Girls
Pizza	7	3
Burgers	5	2

Answer: 5

Answer: 3

5 girls and 2 boys prefer burgers

$5 + 2 = 7$

Answer: 7

Exercise 17A

1   The table shows how many yellow and green circles
    and squares are in a box.

	yellow	green
○	4	5
□	3	6

   a   How many yellow circles?
   b   How many green squares?
   c   How many yellow shapes?   circles *and* squares

2   The table shows how many red and yellow squares
    and triangles are in a box.

	□	△
red	2	5
yellow	3	3

   a   How many red triangles?
   b   How many yellow squares?
   c   How many triangles altogether?

3   The table shows how many boys and girls wore boots
    or shoes.

	boots	shoes
boys	4	4
girls	6	3

   a   How many girls wore boots?
   b   How many boys wore shoes?
   c   How many wore boots altogether?

More columns and rows

Example

Name	Age	Pets
Kayleigh	16	cat
Carol	15	fish
Andrew	16	mouse
Dean	14	dog

a   How old is Andrew?

b   Who has a pet fish?

a   Find the row for Andrew and the column for age.
They meet at 16. Andrew is 16.

Answer: 16

b   Find fish in the pets column.
Go back to the name column for Carol.
Carol has a pet fish.

Answer: Carol

Exercise 17B

1
Name	Age	Height
Jevez	12	152 cm
Sian	13	158 cm
Billy	13	155 cm
Liz	14	157 cm

a   Who is the tallest?

b   What age is Sian?

c   Who has 152 cm height?

2
Name	Age	Pet
Ben	13	dog
Barney	14	dog
Claire	14	cat
Aaron	13	fish
Megan	15	cat
Alex	15	snake
Judy	14	dog

a   Who has a pet snake?

b   What age is Aaron?

c   How many people have pet cats?

Writing tables

Sometimes you will be asked to write information in a table.

Example

Here is a table showing Vitamin C and fibre in vegetables.

Add **peas** to the table. They have **lots** of Vitamin C and **lots** of fibre.

	Vegetables	Vitamin C	Fibre
	cabbage	some	lots
	carrots	lots	some
	spinach	lots	lots
	potatoes	some	some
Answer:	peas	lots	lots

Exercise 17C

Copy and complete these tables.

1

Name	Age	Shoe size
Remi	12	5
Lee	13	6
Barney	13	7

Add Tom to the table. He is 14 and his shoes are size 7.

2

Shape	Colour	Size
rectangle	red	small
circle	blue	big
triangle	red	big

Add a small blue square to the table.

18 Number patterns

On page 165 you saw number sequences that came from patterns of dots. These patterns come from number squares. You need to be able to find the next number in the pattern.

Example

1	2	3	4	5	6	7	8	9	10
11	12	13	14	15	16	17	18	19	20
21	22	23	24	25	26	27	28	29	30
31	32	33	34	35	36	37	38	39	40
41	42	43	44	45	46	47	48	49	50
51	52	53	54	55	56	57	58	59	60
61	62	63	64	65	66	67	68	69	70
71	72	73	74	75	76	77	78	79	80
81	82	83	84	85	86	87	88	89	90
91	92	93	94	95	96	97	98	99	100

List the first 5 shaded numbers.
Explain the pattern.

First number is 5

Count the squares to the next shaded number they go up in steps of 3.

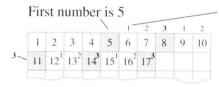

Answer: 5, 8, 11, 14, 17.
They go up in steps of 3.

Exercise 18A

List the first 5 shaded numbers. Explain the pattern.

1

1	2	3	4	5	6	7	8	9	10
11	12	13	14	15	16	17	18	19	20
21	22	23	24	25	26	27	28	29	30
31	32	33	34	35	36	37	38	39	40
41	42	43	44	45	46	47	48	49	50
51	52	53	54	55	56	57	58	59	60
61	62	63	64	65	66	67	68	69	70
71	72	73	74	75	76	77	78	79	80
81	82	83	84	85	86	87	88	89	90
91	92	93	94	95	96	97	98	99	100

2

1	2	3	4	5	6	7	8	9	10
11	12	13	14	15	16	17	18	19	20
21	22	23	24	25	26	27	28	29	30
31	32	33	34	35	36	37	38	39	40
41	42	43	44	45	46	47	48	49	50
51	52	53	54	55	56	57	58	59	60
61	62	63	64	65	66	67	68	69	70
71	72	73	74	75	76	77	78	79	80
81	82	83	84	85	86	87	88	89	90
91	92	93	94	95	96	97	98	99	100

3

1	2	3	4	5	6	7	8	9	10
11	12	13	14	15	16	17	18	19	20
21	22	23	24	25	26	27	28	29	30
31	32	33	34	35	36	37	38	39	40
41	42	43	44	45	46	47	48	49	50
51	52	53	54	55	56	57	58	59	60
61	62	63	64	65	66	67	68	69	70
71	72	73	74	75	76	77	78	79	80
81	82	83	84	85	86	87	88	89	90
91	92	93	94	95	96	97	98	99	100

4

1	2	3	4	5	6	7	8	9	10
11	12	13	14	15	16	17	18	19	20
21	22	23	24	25	26	27	28	29	30
31	32	33	34	35	36	37	38	39	40
41	42	43	44	45	46	47	48	49	50
51	52	53	54	55	56	57	58	59	60
61	62	63	64	65	66	67	68	69	70
71	72	73	74	75	76	77	78	79	80
81	82	83	84	85	86	87	88	89	90
91	92	93	94	95	96	97	98	99	100

If you're given the first number and the pattern to follow, you can work out the sequence.

Example

Start on 4 and go up in 5s.
List 6 numbers.

First number 4, count on 5 to 9,
then 14, 19, 24, 29

1	2	3	4	5	6	7	8	9	10
11	12	13	14	15	16	17	18	19	20
21	22	23	24	25	26	27	28	29	30
31	32	33	34	35	36	37	38	39	40
41	42	43	44	45	46	47	48	49	50
51	52	53	54	55	56	57	58	59	60
61	62	63	64	65	66	67	68	69	70
71	72	73	74	75	76	77	78	79	80
81	82	83	84	85	86	87	88	89	90
91	92	93	94	95	96	97	98	99	100

Answer: 4, 9, 14, 19, 24, 29

Exercise 18B

List 6 numbers in each of these sequences.

1   Start on 6 and go up in 4s.   **2**   Start on 13 and go up in 8s.
3   Start on 15 and go up in 6s.   **4**   Start on 9 and go up in 9s.
5   Start on 7 and go up in 10s.

When the numbers are getting bigger, you need to **add** something each time.

Start on 8 and count on in 2's

8,   10,   12,   14,   16,   …, the next number is 18. Each step **adds 2**.
+2   +2   +2   +2   +2

Example

What comes next? Copy and complete:

9,   11,   13,   15, __, __, __.

Work out what you add each time. These go up in steps of 2.

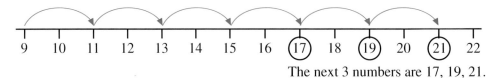

The next 3 numbers are 17, 19, 21.

Answer: 9, 11, 13, 15, <u>17</u>, <u>19</u>, <u>21</u>.

Exercise 18C

What comes next? Copy and complete:

1 4, 6, 8, 10, __ , __ , __ .

2 6, 9, 12, 15, __ , __ , __ .

3 3, 5, 7, 9, __ , __ , __ .

4 5, 10, 15, 20, __ , __ , __ .

5 8, 12, 16, 20, __ , __ , __ .

Example

Fill the gap

1,   4,   7,   10,   —,   16

These go up in steps of 3.

Work out what you add each time.

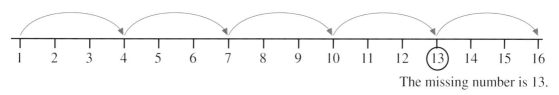

The missing number is 13.

Answer: 1, 4, 7, 10, <u>13</u>, 16.

Exercise 18D

Copy and fill in the gap.

1 2, 5, 8, __ , 14, 17.

2 1, 5, 9, __ , 17, 21.

3 2, 4, 6, __ , 10, 12.

4 1, 3, __ , 7, 9.

5 11, 13, 15, __ , 19, 21.

19 Multiples

To count how much money there is here, count in 2s.

Counting up in 2s: 2, 4, 6, 8. Total 8p

For 5ps count in 5's

Counting up in 5s: 5, 10, 15, 20, 25. Total 25p

For 10ps count in 10s

Counting up in 10s: 10, 20, 30, 40. Total 40p.

5 is 1 lot of 5

10 is 2 lots of 5

15 is 3 lots of 5

5, 10, 15 are all made with lots of 5.
They are called **multiples** of 5.

Another way to work out multiples of 5
is to count from 5 in steps of 5.
You can shade all the multiples of 5
in a 100 square.

You can have multiples of any number.
Multiples of 2 means starting with 2 and
count in steps of 2.
Multiples of 3 means starting with 3 and
count in steps of 3.

1	2	3	4	5	6	7	8	9	10
11	12	13	14	15	16	17	18	19	20
21	22	23	24	25	26	27	28	29	30
31	32	33	34	35	36	37	38	39	40
41	42	43	44	45	46	47	48	49	50
51	52	53	54	55	56	57	58	59	60
61	62	63	64	65	66	67	68	69	70
71	72	73	74	75	76	77	78	79	80
81	82	83	84	85	86	87	88	89	90
91	92	93	94	95	96	97	98	99	100

Example

Write down the first four multiples of 2.

For multiples of 2, start on 2
and count in steps of 2

1	2	1	2	1	2				
1	2	3	4	5	6	7	8	9	10
11	12	13	14	15	16	17	18	19	20

$$2 \xrightarrow{+2} 4 \xrightarrow{+2} 6 \xrightarrow{+2} 8$$

Answer: 2, 4, 6, 8.

Exercise 19A

Write down the first four multiples of:

a 3　　**b** 6　　**c** 10　　**d** 7　　**e** 11

Example

Explain the pattern. Write down the next number.

　　5, 10, 15, 20, ___

These are multiples of 5. They go up in 5s.

Answer:　The next number is 25.

Exercise 19B

Explain the pattern. Write down the next number.

1 4, 8, 12, 16, ___ .　　　　　　**2** 9, 18, 27, 36, ___ .

3 6, 12, 18, 24, ___ .　　　　　**4** 7, 14, 21, 28, ___ .

5 11, 22, 33, 44, ___ .　　　　　**6** 10, 20, 30, 40, ___ .

7 12, 24, 36, 48, ___ .　　　　　**8** 8, 16, 24, 32, ___ .

9 15, 30, 45, 60, ___ .　　　　**10** 20, 40, 60, 80, ___ .

11 100, 200, 300, 400, ___ .　　**12** 25, 50, 75, 100, ___ .

To help you count money in 2ps, 5ps and 10ps,
learn the multiples of 2, 5 and 10.

$1 \times 2 = 2$	$1 \times 5 = 5$	$1 \times 10 = 10$
$2 \times 2 = 4$	$2 \times 5 = 10$	$2 \times 10 = 20$
$3 \times 2 = 6$	$3 \times 5 = 15$	$3 \times 10 = 30$
$4 \times 2 = 8$	$4 \times 5 = 20$	$4 \times 10 = 40$
$5 \times 2 = 10$	$5 \times 5 = 25$	$5 \times 10 = 50$
$6 \times 2 = 12$	$6 \times 5 = 30$	$6 \times 10 = 60$
$7 \times 2 = 14$	$7 \times 5 = 35$	$7 \times 10 = 70$
$8 \times 2 = 16$	$8 \times 5 = 40$	$8 \times 10 = 80$
$9 \times 2 = 18$	$9 \times 5 = 45$	$9 \times 10 = 90$
$10 \times 2 = 20$	$10 \times 5 = 50$	$10 \times 10 = 100$

Here is a multiplication square.

This shows $2 \times 3 = 6$.

2×3 means

2 lots of 3 = 6

×	1	2	3	4	5	6	7	8	9	10
1	1	2	3	4	5	6	7	8	9	10
2	2	4	6	8	10	12	14	16	18	20
3	3	6	9	12	15	18	21	24	27	30
4	4	8	12	16	20	24	28	32	36	40
5	5	10	15	20	25	30	35	40	45	50
6	6	12	18	24	30	36	42	48	54	60
7	7	14	21	28	35	42	49	56	63	70
8	8	16	24	32	40	48	56	64	72	80
9	9	18	27	36	45	54	63	72	81	90
10	10	20	30	40	50	60	70	80	90	100

The numbers in this row and this column are multiples of 2.
2, 4, 6, 8, 10, 12, 14, —.
They are the same as $1 \times 2 = 2$,
$2 \times 2 = 4$ etc.

Example

Use the multiplication square to write the first five multiples of 6.

Multiples of 6 are in this column.

×	1	2	3	4	5	6	7	8	9	10
1	1	2	3	4	5	6	7	8	9	10
2	2	4	6	8	10	12	14	16	18	20
3	3	6	9	12	15	18	21	24	27	30
4	4	8	12	16	20	24	28	32	36	40
5	5	10	15	20	25	30	35	40	45	50
6	6	12	18	24	30	36	42	48	54	60
7	7	14	21	28	35	42	49	56	63	70
8	8	16	24	32	40	48	56	64	72	80
9	9	18	27	36	45	54	63	72	81	90
10	10	20	30	40	50	60	70	80	90	100

Answer: 6, 12, 18, 24, 30

Exercise 19C

Use the multiplication square to write the first five multiples of these:

a 5   **b** 7   **c** 8   **d** 10   **e** 4   **f** 11   **g** 3   **h** 12

Example

Find the answer to 5×6 on the multiplication square.

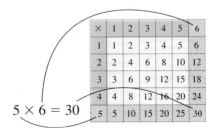

$5 \times 6 = 30$

Answer: $5 \times 6 = 30$

Exercise 19D

Find the answers to these on the multiplication square.

a 6×10	**b** 3×9	**c** 7×8	**d** 9×4	**e** 4×6	**f** 5×7
g 3×4	**h** 6×8	**i** 3×7	**j** 10×10	**k** 7×4	**l** 9×6
m 2×7	**n** 4×8	**o** 10×7	**p** 5×5	**q** 4×4	**r** 9×9

Example

From this list, write down the two numbers that are multiples of 5.

   12, 19, 15, 24, 45, 33

You might recognise the multiples of 5 if you have learned them.

Start on 5 count on in 5s: 5, 10, 15, 20, 25, 30, 35, 40, 45

15 and 45 are in the list.

Answer: 15, 45

Exercise 19E

a From this list write down the two numbers that are multiples of 2:
5, 4, 9, 7, 22, 15, 21

b From this list write down the two numbers that are multiples of 10:
15, 21, 30, 45, 50, 66

c From this list write down the two numbers that are multiples of 5:
14, 29, 30, 57, 63, 25, 72

Remember

To find multiples of 2: Start at 2. Count in steps of 2.

To find multiples of 3: Start at 3. Count in steps of 3.

Multiples of 10 end in 0.
Multiples of 5 end in 5 or 0.
Multiples of 2 are even numbers:
they end in 2, 4, 6, 8 or 0

20 Interpretation

You have already learnt about using tables and graphs. Here is a reminder of how to draw them.

A group of 12 people were asked their favourite sport. Here are the replies.

> football   cricket   cricket   tennis   hockey   football
> football   football   tennis   tennis   football   football

You record them in a table like this.

Sport	Tally	Number
football	ⅢⅠ	6
cricket	‖	2
tennis	‖‖	3
hockey	Ⅰ	1

This shows 6 said football
Remember ⅢⅠ = 5

This shows 1 said hockey

Here is a block graph or bar chart showing this information.

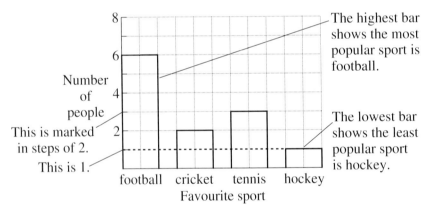

The highest bar shows the most popular sport is football.

The lowest bar shows the least popular sport is hockey.

This is marked in steps of 2.
This is 1.

Number of people

football   cricket   tennis   hockey
Favourite sport

To find how many people were asked about their favourite sport add the values for all the columns:

$$6 + 2 + 3 + 1 = 12$$

football   cricket   tennis   hockey

Scales

In the sports example, the scale for number of people is marked in steps of 2.

Always look carefully at the scale when you read off the values.

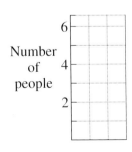

Example

Write the values for the height of each bar shown on these scales.

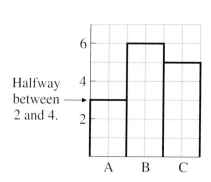 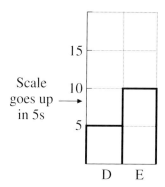

Read across from the top of the bar to each scale.

A: Value is half way between 2 and 4.
    Value is 3.

B: Value is 6.

C: Value is half way between 4 and 6.
    Value is 5.

D: Value is 5.

E: Value is 10.

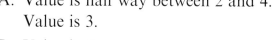

Answer: A 3   B 6   C 5   D 5   E 10

Exercise 20A

Write the values shown on these scales.

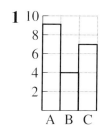 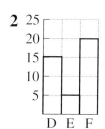 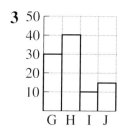

Halfway between 10 and 20 is 15.

Reading bar charts

You can read information from a bar chart.

Example

This bar chart shows the way pupils in Class 11M travel to school.

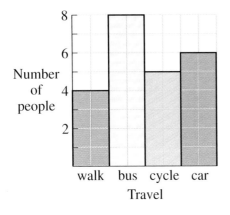

a How do most pupils travel to school?
b How do least pupils get to school?
c How many pupils were asked?

Answer:
a Bus. The bus bar is the highest.
b Walk. The walk bar is the lowest.
c Total of all values is $4 + 8 + 5 + 6 = 23$
  walk bus cycle car

Exercise 20B

1

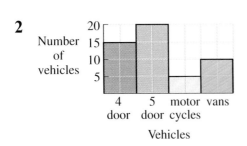

Cards were drawn from a pack and their suit recorded.
a Which suit was drawn most often?
b Which suit was drawn least often?
c How many card were drawn altogether?

2

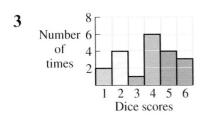

The types of vehicles in a car park were recorded.
a Which vehicles were there most of in the car park?
b Which vehicles were there least of in the car park?
c How many vehicles were in the car park?

3

A dice was rolled and the score recorded.
a Which score happened the most?
b Which score happened the least?
c How many times was the dice rolled?

Experiments

Sometimes you will be asked to do an experiment and record the results in a table and a graph.

Example

Step 1 Flip a coin:

Step 2 Record (H) or tail (T):

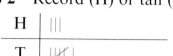

H	|||
T	₩₩|

— Each time you get a head mark | here.

— Each time you get a tail mark | here.

Remember
₩₩ is 5.

Step 3 Draw a bar chart:

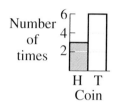

Number of times

H T
Coin

Step 4 What do you notice? Tails happened the most.

Follow the 4 steps: 1. Get results.
2. Record results.
3. Draw a bar chart.
4. Say what you notice.

Exercise 20C

Try these experiments.

Follow the 4 steps above each time.

1 Flip a coin 30 times, record heads/tails.

2 Roll a dice 30 times, record scores 1, 2, 3, 4, 5, 6.

3 Pick a card from a pack 30 times, record suit ♡ ♣ ♢ ♤

4 Ask 20 pupils how they travel to school.

Remember
The tallest column shows what happened the **most**.
The shortest column shows what happened the **least**.

21 Pentagons and hexagons

You need to recognise pentagons and hexagons.

Any shape with
5 sides and 5 vertices
is called a **pentagon**

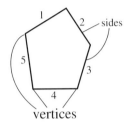

Any shape with
6 sides and 6 vertices
is called a **hexagon**.

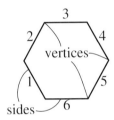

Example

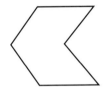

What is this shape called?

Count the vertices: 6
Count the sides: 6   Answer: Hexagon

Exercise 21A

What is each shape called?

1   **2**   **3**

4   **5** 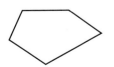   **6**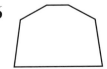

Distances all round

You know how to find the distance all round a rectangle
by adding the lengths of the sides.

You can do the same with pentagons and hexagons.

Example

a Name this shape.

b Find the distance all the way around
the shape.

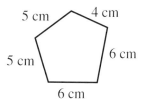

a 5 vertices, 5 sides so it is a pentagon.

Answer: pentagon

b Add the lengths of the 5 sides.

$5 + 4 + 6 + 6 + 5 = 26$ cm

Answer: 26 cm

Exercise 21B

a Name each shape.

b Find the distance all the way around the shape.

1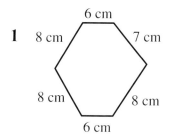

2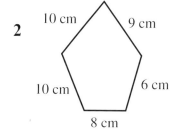

3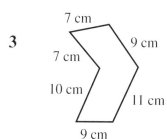

Naming shapes

You can match a shape to its name in a matching diagram.

Example

Complete this matching diagram.

Copy and complete these matching diagrams.

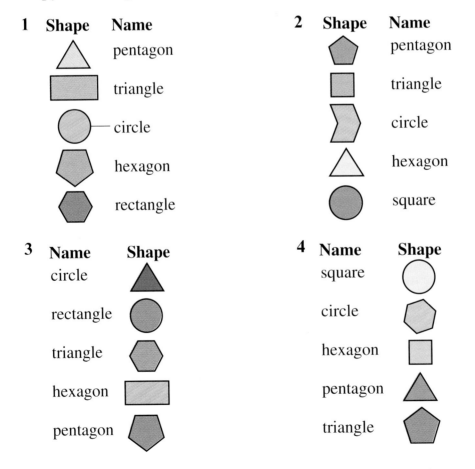

Right angles

Some pentagons and hexagons have right angles.

This pentagon has
3 right angles.

This hexagon has
3 right angles.

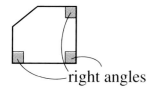

right angles

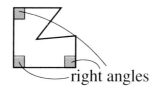

right angles

Reminder
The corner of this
page is a right angle

Example

a Name the shape.
b How many right angles does it have?

Answer: **a** Pentagon
        b 1 right angle

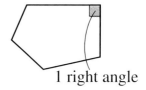

1 right angle

Exercise 21D

a Name each shape.
b How many right angles does it have?

1   2   3   4

Remember
Shapes you should know:

Name	Shape	Vertices	Sides
triangle		3	3
rectangle		4	4
square		4	4
pentagon		5	5
hexagon		6	6

22 Inside out

Three people won the National Lottery one Saturday.
They had to **share** the jackpot.

These pages show you how to share amounts.

When you **share** numbers it is called **division**.
For 10 shared by 2, write $10 \div 2$

Multiplication ($\times$) and division ($\div$) go together.

$2 \times 5 = 10$	$10 \div 2 = 5$	$10 \div 5 = 2$
2 lots of 5	sharing 10 by 2	sharing 10 by 5
total 10	gives 5 each	gives 2 each

You can use the multiplication square to work out
division sums.

$\times$	1	2	3	4	5	6	7	8	9	10
1	1	2	3	4	5	6	7	8	9	10
2	2	4	6	8	10	12	14	16	18	20
3	3	6	9	12	15	18	21	24	27	30
4	4	8	12	16	20	24	28	32	36	40
5	5	10	15	20	25	30	35	40	45	50
6	6	12	18	24	30	36	42	48	54	60
7	7	14	21	28	35	42	49	56	63	70
8	8	16	24	32	40	48	56	64	72	80
9	9	18	27	36	45	54	63	72	81	90
10	10	20	30	40	50	60	70	80	90	100

Find 8 in top row

Look down column for 40

Read across for the answer

To find $40 \div 8$ find 8 in the top row

Look down that column to find 40.
Then read across to find the answer.

$$40 \div 8 = 5$$

Example

Use the multiplication square to find the answer
to $63 \div 7$

×	1	2	3	4	5	6	⑦	8	9	10	
1	1	2	3	4	5	6	7	8	9	10	⟶ Find 7 in top row
2	2	4	6	8	10	12	14	16	18	20	
3	3	6	9	12	15	18	21	24	27	30	
4	4	8	12	16	20	24	28	32	36	40	
5	5	10	15	20	25	30	35	40	45	50	
6	6	12	18	24	30	36	42	48	54	60	
7	7	14	21	28	35	42	49	56	63	70	
8	8	16	24	32	40	48	56	64	72	80	⟶ Look down column for 63
⑨	9	18	27	36	45	54	㉖㉓ 72	81	90		
10	10	20	30	40	50	60	70	80	90	100	⟶ Read off 9

Answer: $63 \div 7 = 9$

Exercise 22A

Use the multiplication square to find:

a $88 \div 11$ **b** $24 \div 3$ **c** $70 \div 10$
d $99 \div 11$ **e** $35 \div 5$ **f** $32 \div 8$
g $18 \div 2$ **h** $20 \div 4$ **i** $21 \div 7$
j $12 \div 2$ **k** $40 \div 4$ **l** $54 \div 6$
m $27 \div 9$ **n** $24 \div 4$ **o** $63 \div 9$
p $42 \div 6$ **q** $56 \div 7$ **r** $48 \div 6$

Using a calculator

You can use a calculator to work out division sums.

Example

Find $27 \div 3$

Key in   2 7 ÷ 3 =

The answer is

Answer: $27 \div 3 = 9$

Exercise 22B

1   Use a calculator to check your answers to
    Exercise 22A.

2   Use the multiplication square to find:

    a $25 \div 5$ **b** $36 \div 6$ **c** $16 \div 4$
    d $81 \div 9$ **e** $100 \div 10$

    Check your answers with a calculator.
    What do you notice?

Multiplication and division pairs

You saw on page 222 that multiplication and division go
together.
For each multiplication there is a division pair.
If you know the multiplication, you can work out the
divisions from the pattern.

    $4 \times 5 = 20$
    $20 \div 5 = 4$ Use the numbers 20, 5, 4 each time.
    $20 \div 4 = 5$

Example

    $5 \times 10 = 50$

Copy and fill in the missing numbers.

a $50 \div \Box = 5$

b $50 \div \Box = 10$

Look at the multiplication to see which number is
missing in the division.

Answer:

a $50 \div \boxed{10} = 5$

b $50 \div \boxed{5} = 10$

Exercise 22C

Copy and fill in the missing numbers.

1 $4 \times 10 = 40$
$40 \div \square = 4$
$40 \div \square = 10$

2 $3 \times 5 = 15$
$15 \div 5 = \square$
$15 \div \square = 5$

3 $2 \times 8 = 16$
$16 \div \square = 2$
$\square \div 2 = 8$

4 $3 \times 10 = 30$
$\square \div 3 = 10$
$30 \div \square = 3$

5 $2 \times 7 = 14$
$\square \div 2 = 7$
$14 \div \square = 2$

6 $4 \times 3 = 12$
$\square \div 3 = 4$
$12 \div \square = 3$

7 $6 \times 3 = 18$
$18 \div 6 = \square$
$18 \div 3 = \square$

8 $7 \times 4 = 28$
$28 \div 4 = \square$
$28 \div \square = 4$

9 $8 \times 6 = 48$
$48 \div 8 = \square$
$48 \div 6 = \square$

10 $5 \times 7 = 35$
$35 \div \square = 5$
$35 \div \square = 7$

11 $3 \times 8 = 24$
$24 \div \square = 8$
$\square \div 8 = 3$

12 $7 \times 9 = 63$
$63 \div \square = 9$
$63 \div 9 = \square$

Remember

Learn these division facts:

$2 \div 2 = 1$	$5 \div 5 = 1$	$10 \div 10 = 1$
$4 \div 2 = 2$	$10 \div 5 = 2$	$20 \div 10 = 2$
$6 \div 2 = 3$	$15 \div 5 = 3$	$30 \div 10 = 3$
$8 \div 2 = 4$	$20 \div 5 = 4$	$40 \div 10 = 4$
$10 \div 2 = 5$	$25 \div 5 = 5$	$50 \div 10 = 5$
$12 \div 2 = 6$	$30 \div 5 = 6$	$60 \div 10 = 6$
$14 \div 2 = 7$	$35 \div 5 = 7$	$70 \div 10 = 7$
$16 \div 2 = 8$	$40 \div 5 = 8$	$80 \div 10 = 8$
$18 \div 2 = 9$	$45 \div 5 = 9$	$90 \div 10 = 9$
$20 \div 2 = 10$	$50 \div 5 = 10$	$100 \div 10 = 10.$

23 Remainders

Sometimes when you share objects they do not share exactly and there are some left over.

Oranges cost 8p each.
How many can you buy with 35p?

8p each

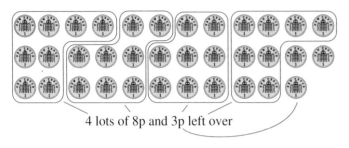

4 lots of 8p and 3p left over

You can buy 4 oranges and have 3p left.
The 3p is called the **remainder**.

Using a calculator: $35 \div 8 = 4.375$
4.375 means 4 oranges and some left over

> You cannot buy part of an orange, so 4.375 is not a sensible answer.

To find how much is left over: work out $8p \times 4 = 32p$
$35p - 32p = 3p$, so 3p is left over.
You write $35 \div 8 = 4$ remainder 3

Example

25 pencils shared between 4 people.
How many for each person? How many left over?
Using a calculator:

$25 \div 4 = 6.25$ This means 6 pencils each and some left over.

$6 \times 4 = 24$ 6 people with 4 pencils each is 24 pencils

There were 25 pencils, $25 - 24 = 1$ so 1 is left over.

Answer: 4 pencils, 1 left over

Exercise 23A

1   How many 5p sweets can be bought, and how much left over, from:
    a 26p   **b** 33p   **c** 28p   **d** 94p   **e** 53p   **f** 45p

5p each

2   How many 8p wafers can be bought, and how much left over, from:
    a 20p   **b** 50p   **c** 25p   **d** 45p   **e** 95p   **f** 47p

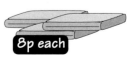
8p each

Example

How many 6p notelets can be bought with 45p? How much remains? This means 'how much money left over?'

$45 \div 6 = 7.5$ $\begin{array}{l} 7 \times 6 = 42p \\ 45p - 42p = 3p \end{array}$ Answer: 7 notelets remainder 3p

Exercise 23B

1   How many 6p apples can be bought, and how much remains, with:
   a 27p   **b** 44p   **c** 69p   **d** 40p   **e** 50p

2   How many 9p ices can be bought, and how much remains, with:
   a 50p   **b** 75p   **c** 48p   **d** 92p   **e** 55p

3   How many 7p ginger biscuits can be bought, and how much remains, with:
   a 25p   **b** 50p   **c** 75p   **d** 48p   **e** 90p

Example

Eggs are packed in boxes of 6. How many boxes are needed for 34 eggs?

$34 \div 6 = 5.66666667$
$6 \times 5 = 30$
$34 - 30 = 4$

Answer: 5 boxes, 4 eggs left over

Exercise 23C

1   Eggs are packed in boxes of 6.
   How many boxes are needed for:
   a 28 eggs   **b** 43 eggs   **c** 70 eggs   **d** 39 eggs   **e** 50 eggs

2   Light bulbs are packed in boxes of 4.
   How many boxes are needed for:
   a 47 bulbs   **b** 31 bulbs   **c** 70 bulbs
   d 18 bulbs   **e** 26 bulbs

3   Cream cakes are packed in boxes of 3.
   How many boxes are needed for:
   a 14 cakes   **b** 21 cakes   **c** 32 cakes   **d** 49 cakes   **e** 29 cakes

24 3-D shapes

3-D shapes are also called solid shapes.
You need to be able to recognise and name these solids.

Cylinder

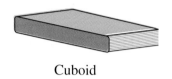

Cuboid

Cube

Sphere

Examples

Name an article that looks like a sphere.

Answer: An orange

Name an article that looks like a cube.

Answer: An oxo cube

Exercise 24A

Name an article that looks like these solids:

a a cube   **b** a cuboid   **c** a cylinder   **d** a sphere

Here is another 3-D shape

This shape has:
6 vertices
5 faces
9 edges

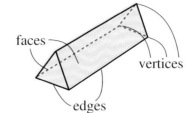

Vertices are
corners.

The dotted lines show
the hidden edges.
Count these too.

Example

This shape has how many
a vertices   **b** faces   **c** edges?

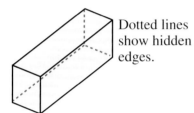

Dotted lines
show hidden
edges.

Answer: 8 vertices
           6 faces
          12 edges

Exercise 24B

These shapes have how many
a vertices   **b** faces   **c** edges?

1

2
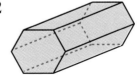

3

4

25 Match it

You know how to match names to objects in a matching diagram. Here are some reminders.
Here is a matching diagram.

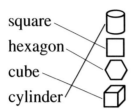

Each name belongs to one of the shapes.

Example

Complete this matching diagram:

1 line symmetry
2 lines symmetry
3 lines symmetry

Answer:

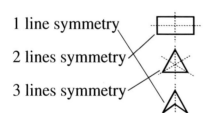

Exercise 25A

Copy and complete these matching diagrams:

a 3   6
   5   3
   12   5
   6   12

b multiple of 3   25
   multiple of 5   4
   multiple of 2   9

c square
   triangle
   cube

This matching diagram shows pupils' ages.

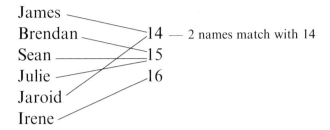

2 names match with 14

It shows that James and Jaroid are both 14.
Three pupils are 15, Irene is 16.

Example

Copy and complete:

$$3$$

multiple of 3   6
multiple of 2   9
           4

The multiples of 3 in the list are 3, 6, 9.
The multiples of 2 in the list are 6 and 4.

Answer: multiple of 3 ⟨ 3
         multiple of 2 ⟨ 6
                      9
                     4

Exercise 25B

Copy and complete these diagrams:

a
               2
even   5
odd   6
              9
            10

b   0 right angles   □

       1 right angle

       4 right angles   ▭

c
                   25
multiple of 2   9
multiple of 3   15
multiple of 5   8
                   10

Reading matching diagrams

Sometimes you will be asked to find information from a matching diagram.

Example

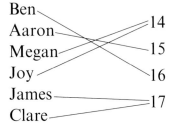

a How old is Megan?
b How many people are 17?
c Who is 15?

Answer: a Megan is 14.   The arrow goes from Megan to 14.
b 2 people are 17.   The arrows from James and Clare go to 17.
c Aaron is 15.   Find 15 and follow the arrow back to Aaron.

Exercise 25C

1
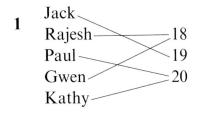

a How old is Kathy?
b How many people are 18?
c Who is 19?

2

    multiple of 4 ——— 25
                      18
    odd ————
                    ← 6
    multiple of 6 ——
                      20

a Which number is a multiple of 4?
b How many numbers are multiples of 6?

3

    0 right angles ——
    2 right angles ——
    4 right angles ——

a How many shapes have 4 right angles?
b How many shapes have 2 right angles?

26 Exploring connections

This page shows you short cuts for working out
multiplication and division sums.

×	1	2	3	4	5	6	7	8	9	10
1	1	2	3	4	5	6	7	8	9	10
2	2	4	6	8	10	12	14	16	18	20
3	3	6	9	12	15	18	21	24	27	30
4	4	8	12	16	20	24	28	32	36	40
5	5	10	15	20	25	30	35	40	45	50
6	6	12	18	24	30	36	42	48	54	60
7	7	14	21	28	35	42	49	56	63	70
8	8	16	24	32	40	48	56	64	72	80
9	9	18	27	36	45	54	63	72	81	90
10	10	20	30	40	50	60	70	80	90	100

These are   These are
multiples of 2   multiples of 4

Look at the shaded columns to see that the
multiples of 4 are also multiples of 2.
The multiples of 4 are **twice** the multiples of 2.

multiples of 2		multiples of 4
2	$\times 2 =$	4
4	$\times 2 =$	8
6	$\times 2 =$	12
8	$\times 2 =$	16
10	$\times 2 =$	20
$\vdots$	$\times 2 =$	$\vdots$

This is because 4 is twice 2, $4 = 2 \times 2$
So if you know the multiples of 2, you can work out multiples of 4.

Multiples of 2 are **half** the multiples of 4.

multiples of 4		multiples of 2
4	$\div 2 =$	2
8	$\div 2 =$	4
12	$\div 2 =$	6
16	$\div 2 =$	8
20	$\div 2 =$	10
$\vdots$	$\div 2 =$	$\vdots$

Example

Work out 4×4 in your head.

4×4 is twice 2×4

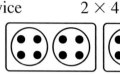

You know $2 \times 4 = 8$
so 4×4 is $8 \times 2 = 16$

4 lots of 4   2 lots of 4   2 lots of 4
                         = 8   = 8

Answer: 16

Exercise 26A

Work these out in your head.

1   **a** 3×2 **b** 5×2 **c** 10×2 **d** 6×2 **e** 7×2

2   **a** 3×4 **b** 5×4 **c** 10×4 **d** 6×4 **e** 7×4

Example

Write the multiples of 2 and the multiples of 6. What is the connection?

Use the multiplication square to help.

multiples of 2		multiples of 6
2	$\times 3 =$	6
4	$\times 3 =$	12
6	$\times 3 =$	18
8	$\times 3 =$	24
10	$\times 3 =$	30

The first 5 are enough.

×	1	2	3	4	5	6	7	8	9	10
1	1	2	3	4	5	6	7	8	9	10
2	2	4	6	8	10	12	14	16	18	20
3	3	6	9	12	15	18	21	24	27	30
4	4	8	12	16	20	24	28	32	36	40
5	5	10	15	20	25	30	35	40	45	50
6	6	12	18	24	30	36	42	48	54	60
7	7	14	21	28	35	42	49	56	63	70
8	8	16	24	32	40	48	56	64	72	80
9	9	18	27	36	45	54	63	72	81	90
10	10	20	30	40	50	60	70	80	90	100

Answer: The multiples of 6 are **3 times** the multiples of 2.

Exercise 26B

1   Write the multiples of 4 and the multiples of 8. What is the connection?

2   Write the multiples of 3 and the multiples of 9. What is the connection?

3   Write the multiples of 5 and the multiples of 10. What is the connection?

4   Write the multiples of 2 and the multiples of 8. What is the connection?